A
Worcestershire
Christmas

A
Worcestershire
Christmas

Compiled by David Green

ALAN SUTTON

First published in the United Kingdom in 1991 by
Alan Sutton Publishing Ltd · Phoenix Mill · Far Thrupp
Stroud · Gloucestershire

First published in the United States of America in 1992 by
Alan Sutton Publishing Inc · Wolfeboro Falls
NH 03896–0848

Copyright © this compilation, David Green 1991

All rights reserved. No part of this publication may be
reproduced, stored in a retrieval system, or transmitted, in
any form or by any means, electronic, mechanical,
photocopying, recording or otherwise, without the prior
permission of the publishers and copyright holders.

British Library Cataloguing in Publication Data

Green, David John Norton, *1930–*
A Worcestershire Christmas.
I. Title
820.8033

ISBN 0–86299–930–8

**Library of Congress Cataloging in Publication Data
applied for**

Cover illustration: Bringing home the winter firewood *by
Anonymous. (Photograph: Fine Art Photographs & Library Ltd.)*

Typeset in Garamond 12/13.
Typesetting and origination by
Alan Sutton Publishing Limited.
Printed in Great Britain by
The Bath Press, Bath, Avon.

Contents

· A Worcestershire Christmas ·

· A Worcestershire Christmas ·

· *A Worcestershire Christmas* ·

Christmas in the Good Old Days

FRED ARCHER

Few, if any, contemporary writers have written more evocatively about rural Worcestershire in days gone by, than Fred Archer, who lived and worked on the family farm at Ashton-under-Hill in the Vale of Evesham. With many books to his credit, as well as countless articles in magazines and newspapers, he has vividly brought to life, season by season, the characters and customs of the countryside he knew so well. In this first extract from Fred Archer's reminiscences, he looks back to one of the first childhood Christmases at Ashton-under-Hill he can recall, when the 'Christmas tree' was a laurel branch and his main present was a tin drum.

The first Christmas I really remember was in 1921. A few days before, Dad, Mother, my brother and sister and I went into Evesham to do our Christmas shopping. Dad drove Polly, our chestnut mare, with the governess cart, and when we reached Evesham he gave a penny to a little boy outside the King's Head to hold the reins while we shopped. Dad and Mother went to Cox's, the grocer, and bought some of the goodies for Christmas, including a sack of oranges for the carol singers, and plenty of nuts. Dad liked brazils so we had lots of these!

'The butchers' and poulterers' shops were always a sight to
see, with game and poultry and rabbits displayed in
tempting rows to catch the eye of the Christmas shopper'

The butchers' and poulterers' shops in those days were always a
sight to see, with game and poultry and rabbits displayed in
tempting rows to catch the eye of the Christmas shopper.

Two days before Christmas our first carol singers arrived
after tea. They were two little boys. After the first verse of
'While Shepherds Watched Their Flocks' Dad asked them
inside our candlelit hall. They sang the other verses and Dad
gave them a penny each and one of the oranges from the
sack.

During that week before Christmas, local teenagers were
scaling the trees on Bredon Hill for mistletoe. There were
massive boughs of mistletoe high up on the poplars of Grafton
Coppice, although some of the best came from the hawthorn

2

bushes and the cider apple trees. There was money to be made with mistletoe at Evesham market.

At the post office-cum-shop run by Mr and Mrs Tandy, there was a modest-sized window and it was decorated with crackers, silver balls, bunting, boxes of dates and figs. When the oil lamps in the window were lit about tea-time, the Christmas fare on display looked like a little fairyland, and there were even cardboard Father Christmases fixed to both sides of the window frames. Mr Tandy had already been busy taking the mail round the village, but his big day was Christmas Day itself, when the bulk of the cards and presents were delivered.

On Christmas Eve, Uncle Jim arrived from his home in Coalville, and after dark, when Dad had put up our 'Christmas tree', which was a branch of the laurel bush, we sat by the fire and listened to Uncle's many tales.

Uncle's tales went on until bed-time; tales of Spring-Heeled Jack who eerily stood in Rabbit Lane on moonlit nights; and of the Will of the Wisp he saw by the brook in the early mornings when he fetched the Squire's horses in for work.

I remember going to bed about 7.30 and trying to sleep while thinking about Spring-Heeled Jack. Later the stairs creaked and there was a flicker of candlelight as someone came into my bedroom. It was Dad doing his Father Christmas act, and I pretended to be sleeping as he filled my stocking.

It was just getting light on Christmas morning when I eventually woke up and I started making a din on the tin drum which lay at the foot of the bed. It was my main present.

I remember Uncle Jim and Dad frying bacon and eggs for breakfast in a large frying pan which hung from a chain over the fire. Then, after breakfast, the grown-ups started getting the dinner ready. That year we had a suckling pig, with potatoes, sprouts and other vegetables, followed by Christmas pudding and mince pies.

A children's drum and fife band playing carols around the
the turn of the century. Groups such as this were once a
familiar sight in the Bredon Hill villages

We didn't usually go to chapel on Christmas Day, but we
always went as a family on the Sunday before and the Sunday
after.

During the morning Mr Tandy came with some more cards
after I had heard the horse-drawn mail van arriving at his shop
from Tewkesbury driven by old Charlie Booth. 'Three half
pence for twopence' his horse's hooves seemed to be saying as
they came up the Beckford road. Charlie usually stayed in the
village all day long and did some gardening, before returning
with the evening post.

After dinner Dad brought in the phonograph and set it up
on the dining-room table. He fetched some of his cylinder-
shaped records and wound up the machine. Each record began
with the words: 'This is an Edison Bell record'. Then the tunes
were scratched out on the celluloid.

4

Before tea Auntie Annie came round with her homemade chocolate – and that was a real treat. Then for tea we had pink celery, a blancmange made in a lion mould, trifle and Christmas cake. The grown-ups played dominoes and there were various different card games, although these were not played with the standard playing cards which were known as the Devil's cards by the chapel people! Then our candles were lit and it was off to bed again.

Boxing Day was usually spent rabbiting on Bredon Hill. Dad would go up there with some of his friends, but I wasn't old enough to join them and occupied the day beating my drum and playing snakes and ladders with my brother.

Late on Boxing Day evening a group of carol singers arrived. They sang many of the old Christmas carols, including one which was arranged by Amy Roberson, the organist at St Barbara's, the parish church at Ashton-under-Hill. I still have the words with me now:

> Hark what news the angels bring.
> All hail and praise the sacred morn.
> Arise ye sleepy souls arise.

A Season for Spectres

RAYMOND LAMONT BROWN

Traditionally, Christmas has always been a time for recounting ghost stories. What more fitting atmosphere for listening to tales of the supernatural than in the warmth of a blazing log fire, with shadows flickering on the walls and the howl of a winter gale rattling the doors and windows? A writer who has related many a Worcestershire ghost story is Raymond Lamont Brown, and this selection comes from collections published in 1966 and 1977.

Down the lane leading to the Vale of Evesham village of Childswickham it rattled – the hearse without a driver. Not stopping when it came to the houses, the black vehicle rattled on to the church. Louis Lefevre galloped after it hoping to arrest its crazy course. At last he caught up with it at the church gate; the horses nodding their black plumes and jingling their harnesses. But in the time it took Lefevre to dismount – the hearse was only out of his sight a second or two – it had vanished, mysteriously and completely.

Was it a ghost that Lefevre had seen? He certainly thought so, and noted it down in his tour of England notes which were published privately in Paris in 1807. No-one I asked in modern Childswickham could recall any mention of a phantom hearse, but several others had fascinating stories to tell of the haunted churches of Worcestershire.

One story I heard in The Chequers Inn at Crowle, concerns the largely Victorian rebuilt parish church of St John the Baptist. It appears that late in the year 1844 Charlie Price, the grave-digger's assistant, had to go into Worcester to pick up a new specially-made spade for the churchyard tool kit. Never a man to pass up an opportunity to dawdle, Charlie had ensconced himself for the evening in one of the famous Worcester hostelries, before walking back to Crowle.

Charlie Price was nearly home – he lived in a cottage near Crowle Court Farm – when a person stepped out in front of him and stopped him with a raised arm. In the moonlight Charlie could make out what looked like a monk's figure. Slowly a hand appeared from one of the sleeves of the monk's habit and beckoned for Charlie to follow. Not likely, thought Charlie to himself and made to run away, the new spade still over his shoulder. To his horror he found that his legs would not obey him and some strange forces began to impel him along the track towards the church, in the wake of the disappearing monk.

Charlie's legs walked briskly carrying his unwilling body after the monk. As the figure strode through pools of moonlight, the grave-digger's assistant could see that it was very tall and was dressed in a black habit.

At last they arrived at the churchyard. Not stopping, the strange monk passed right through the churchyard wall and on to the mounded grass. Charlie felt sick, but his legs clambered him over the wall. After a while the monk stopped and Charlie found himself within two feet of the figure. He began to feel the strange propelling power leave his legs which now began to tremble.

The ghostly monk – mortals don't pass through walls

Charlie's numbed mind registered – pointed to the spade and then to the ground. He was to dig. Not wanting his arms to take up the same strange locomotion as his legs, Charlie dug.

He dug down for a foot or two and then struck a hard object. He cleared the soil and came across a large lump. In the dark he could not see what the object was, but looked up hoping for some clue from the monk, but the figure had vanished – almost as quickly as Charlie now did, home!

Next morning Charlie and the grave-digger cautiously approached the hole Charlie had dug. Together they dragged a stone on to the grass; later, experts averred that the stone Charlie had found – which turned out to be a stone lectern – had originally come from the Benedictine abbey of Evesham. Today the lectern is one of the prize possessions of St John the Baptist's Church at Crowle. But few know that its discovery may have been because of a ghost. Alas no-one, it seems, ever believed Charlie's story.

Abbey Thorpe used to lodge with her mother in a seedy alehouse next to a newspaper shop in Dudley's High Street (the site of the present Three Crowns). To earn a penny or two, she used to clean at St Edmund's Church, and one Sunday morning she was up a ladder dusting a ledge, when she saw a girl she knew vaguely, as she lived in the next street. The girl entered the church and sat down at the end of the front pew.

Getting down from the ladder, Abbey went over to the girl, who was very pale and seemed to be in a fever. Abbey enquired if she was well, and the girl asked if she could have a glass of water. Abbey went to get the water, but when she returned the girl had gone.

When Abbey went home at midday, her mother was full of the news that an epidemic was likely, as a girl in the next street had died that morning of a contagious fever.

'Was it that Anne Simon?' asked Abbey. 'Yes,' her mother

replied, 'she died around ten this morning. How did you know.' Abbey told her what she had seen in the church.

Abbey couldn't eat her frugal lunch that day, for she remembered that the town clocks had struck ten when she went to get the glass of water for the girl. Abbey – or anyone else – never did find out why Anne Simon had materialised in St Edmund's at the very moment of her death.

In his book *The Certainty of the World of Spirits*, Richard Baxter writes that during the time of the Civil War he was on guard duty at Worcester Cathedral when he was badly frightened by the ghostly appearance of a phantom bear, which danced in chains. Parallels of bears' ghosts have been recorded on the Chelsea Embankment and at the Tower of London. What they signify is hard to say, but evil usually walks hand-in-hand with the occult, so that cruelty to animals may find an outlet in a manifestation of the occult.

Perhaps the most strange story comes from the conversations of a lady who once visited St Helen's Church in Worcester. The lady, who was interested in ecclesiastical furniture, was examining the church fittings when she saw a little girl on her knees in the aisle, obviously looking for something. As the child was sobbing, the lady offered to help her look for what was apparently lost. As the lady spoke the child got up and ran towards the chancel door, but before reaching the door the child disappeared into the air.

The lady was getting on in years and thought that the child's abrupt departure was because of her own deterioration of sight. She paid no more attention to it and continued to study the furniture. Later she remembered, and asked the vicar of the church who the child was. 'For a number of years,' the vicar explained, 'people have seen this girl in the church; she is always searching for something and disappears in the same way on being spoken to. I have no idea who or what she is!'

Whether you happen to believe in ghosts or not, there is

always a sincerity in the records of the past. At the time, people *knew* what they had seen; they were sure in their own minds *what* they had seen. Even today there are many physical and spiritual laws that we do not understand.

from

The Poems of A.E. Housman

Although Alfred Edward Housman is probably best remembered for his epic poem A Shropshire Lad, *he was, in fact, a son of Worcestershire having been born in the village of Fockbury, near Bromsgrove in 1859. Soon after his birth, the family moved to Perry Hall in Bromsgrove, now a hotel, and the young Alfred attended Bromsgrove School where, at the age of eighteen, he became head boy. The following expressive verses reflecting a winter episode in* A Shropshire Lad, *typify the deep love of the countryside which preoccupied him in much of his writing.*

Bring, in this timeless grave to throw,
No cypress, sombre on the snow;
Snap not from the bitter yew
His leaves that live December through;

· A Worcestershire Christmas ·

Break no rosemary, bright with rime
And sparkling to the cruel clime;
Nor plod the winter land to look
For willows in the icy brook
To cast them leafless round him: bring
No spray that ever buds in spring.

But if the Christmas field has kept
Awns the last gleaner overstept,
Or shrivelled flax, whose flower is blue
A single season, never two;
Or if one haulm whose year is o'er
Shivers on the upland frore,
Oh, bring from hill and stream and plain
Whatever will not flower again,
To give him comfort: he and those
Shall bide eternal bedfellows
Where low upon the couch he lies
Whence he never shall arise.

Also from A Shropshire Lad *is what many regard as Housman's best-known verse, 'Bredon Hill'. He had a special affection for this gently sloping outlier of the Cotswolds overlooking the Vale of Evesham, and the word-picture he paints of it is as true to life today as it was when he wrote it. All seven verses of this poignant work are reproduced here, so that the fifth verse which alludes to Bredon at Christmastime, can be appreciated in its proper context.*

In summertime on Bredon
The bells they sound so clear;
Round both the shires they ring them
In steeples far and near,
A happy noise to hear.

The Worcestershire poet Alfred Edward Housman. His
association with his native Bromsgrove is still proudly
remembered

Here of a Sunday morning
My love and I would lie,
And see the coloured counties,
And hear the larks so high
About us in the sky.

The bells would ring to call her
In valleys miles away:
'Come to church, good people;
Good people, come and pray'.
But here my love would stay.

12

And I would turn and answer
Among the springing thyme,
'Oh, peal upon our wedding,
And we will hear the chime,
And come to church in time.'

But when the snows at Christmas
On Bredon top were strown,
My love rose up so early
And stole out unbeknown
And went to church alone.

They tolled the one bell only,
Groom there was none to see,
The mourners followed after,
And so to church went she,
And would not wait for me.

The bells they sound on Bredon,
And still the steeples hum.
'Come all to church, good people',
Oh, noisy bells be dumb;
I hear you, I will come.

Roll on Christmas

GILBERT MOORE

One of the highlights of the Christmas celebrations of 1909 was the new craze of roller-skating, and special rinks were being opened all over the Midlands, so that the ever-increasing number of enthusiasts could indulge in this energetic activity. There was a rink in Worcester and another in Malvern, and many skaters made the short journey to enjoy the wide choice of rinks in Birmingham, part of which was then in Worcestershire. Writing in 1967, Gilbert Moore offered this seasonal review of the extraordinary phenomenon which had overtaken Edwardian England.

Viewed from the Christmas of 1909, the year had been a momentous one. Bleriot had flown the Channel, and the *Daily Mail* had organised the first night flight, from London to Manchester. A revolution in Morocco had set the Moors and the Spanish at each other's throats; bickering between Bulgaria and Austria threatened the peace of the world. But what did the British public care? It was too drunk that festive season with the new craze of roller-skating.

Nothing could shake the skating English off their balance. The new sport, which had been growing as the Edwardian era closed, was the rage of the Christmas season of 1909. By then, no self-respecting town was without one of the new Roller

Rinks, and the Midlands, with its concentration of humanity, had more than most.

Birmingham's City Rink and Winter Gardens were situated near New Street railway station and what was described as the Electric Car routes. In its prospectus, issued earlier that year, the rink anticipated an annual profit of £8,400. This was to be derived from two hundred afternoon admissions and eight hundred evening admissions at one shilling each, and from refreshments, carnivals and tuition fees. From the success of the rink, its ambition must have been more than realised.

It was Mr J.T. Cooper of the Birmingham Roller Skating Club who that New Year won the one-mile amateur championship in 3 minutes 45 seconds. The race was run at the neigbouring West Bromwich Rink before five hundred spectators. They had not been deterred by the blizzards and gales, for the eighteen thousand square feet of floor space at the West Bromwich Rink was electrically heated, claiming to be the largest in the Midlands.

At the same time, nearby Smethwick considered itself 'un-challenged' though it had no heated floor. During the Christmas week, they held a Grand Sports Night in aid of the Smethwick Poor Children's Treat and Boot Fund (there were those who could not even afford boots that Christmas, let alone frivolous appendages with wheels) and staged a roller-skating hockey match between the Dudley and Smethwick Clubs.

There seem to have been as many diversions on roller skates, as at present there are on ice: pierrot shows, fancy dress parades and carnivals. Stunts of all kinds, with see-saws and barrels, were performed on rollers during the mania, and races were run against bicycles. Elaborate dance routines followed the regulations of the National Skating Association, which directed the steps, timing and movement.

But few rinks can have outshone the Lozells and Erdington Rink in the matter of showmanship, under the guidance of a

15

handsome and distinguished young man, Mr A.T.C. Bridges. His experience included not only the managership of rinks in Vienna, Paris and Milan, but he was an actor of some success.

The rink claimed that its staff was the most expert, civil and obliging one could contact. The rink itself (said the rink) was the best conducted in the Midlands; one's daughter could attend without fear of being insulted by undesirables. One's daughter could, however, be enticed to the rink by the looks and charm of Mr Bridges, as no doubt much of the public was. And this sense of theatre was a great asset to productions like the Pierrot and Pierrette Carnival of that Christmas of 1909, and to the fancy dress ball held for the Chester Road Cricket and Hockey Club, which two thousand spectators attended, 450 in costume.

Aston also had a rink at the Lower Grounds, a general entertainment centre which once was host to Buffalo Bill and the Deadwood Stage. The proprietors of the rink called the attention of principals of educational establishments to the rink's invigorating exercise, but were apprehensive about the horseplay that went on in other parts of the Lower Grounds. A cautionary set of rules included: 'Gentlemen without Ladies should not trespass on the time or space set apart for Ladies. No skater should stop on circuit, except to assist a Lady'.

No such problem burdened Worcester's Arboretum, an aristocrat of a rink, where they skidded round in evening dress. Malvern's rink had a carnival that Christmas, and Birmingham's Spring Hill called its American rink, 'the Rendezvous of the Elite'. Another city rink was in Sparkbrook. Handsworth (then a borough) had a roller rink some years before the Rage, and was well-equipped to absorb the sudden onslaught. At Edgbaston Rink, a growing success, they skated to the music of a military band.

Where *wasn't* there a rink? A shortage of turkeys there may have been that Christmas, but not of roller rinks. The music

hall had made great strides that year, and the sixpenny hop was a tradition, but the Rinking Rage out-fevered them both. The Liberals and the Radicals were beating their chests in readiness for the general election; but the electors were deaf to all but the song of the rollers. While the government still tinkered with thoughts of old age pensions and labour exchanges, the public was getting its skates on.

Perhaps it was all an unconscious breakaway from the frills and furbelows of Edwardiana; from its restrictive elegance on the one hand, and repressive poverty on the other. Or maybe it was that the exhilarating speed of the horse-less carriage, prohibitive to most at a running cost of £2 10s. a week, could be best imitated on a pair of skates, hired for a modest sixpence a night.

This Baby Business at Bethlehem

MERVYN CHARLES-EDWARDS

The Right Reverend Mervyn Charles-Edwards was Bishop of Worcester from 1956 to 1970. His official residence was Hartlebury Castle near Kidderminster, seat of the Bishops of Worcester since the 1200s, and it was in this historic setting in 1963 that he penned these thoughts about the essence and meaning of the Christmas story.

· *A Worcestershire Christmas* ·

The Right Reverend Mervyn Charles-Edwards, Bishop of
Worcester from 1956 to 1970

It's this baby in a stable that gets me. The rest of Christmas is
easy to understand. It's life, it's fun, the family being
together, filling the children's stockings, presents and plum
pudding, kissing under the mistletoe and candles on the tree.
But this baby business at Bethlehem – what does it mean? – all
this talk about peace on Earth and goodwill, when nearly a
quarter of the world's population is always hungry, and bomb
production seems more important than bread distribution.

We keep Christmas, we are told, because it is Christ's
birthday, and that is certainly what we sing about in our carols:

> In the bleak mid-winter
> A stable-place sufficed
> The Lord God Almighty,
> Jesus Christ.

Worcester Cathedral, mother church of an ancient diocese,
was begun in 1084 by St Wulfstan, although its site was
occupied by a place of worship as early as the seventh
century

Fact or fiction, it's a lovely story – or is it? When I visited my youngest grandchild recently in the modern maternity wing of the hospital, I wondered what childbirth must have been like in a dirty cowshed, and when Sister said, 'Only two visitors at a time, please, and not for long', I could not help thinking what her reactions would have been if a number of noisy shepherds had suddenly burst in, saying they had seen a vision of angels.

I suppose it's the way we are made; we can be sentimental about Christmas, pull another cracker, wear a paper hat and take a second mince pie for a lucky month, or we can be horrible realists, and amid all the fun and games still have at the back of our mind the knowledge that what we are really commemorating is the unpleasant fact that nobody really wanted Mary, Joseph and Jesus. Like all refugees they were a nuisance, demanding civil rights and yet not fitting into the ordered community life of Bethlehem.

At any rate, the authorities soon cleared them out, and the Christmas story which begins with the coming of the Holy Family to Bethlehem ends with their flight to Egypt. This seemed a very satisfactory solution to a tiresome problem, and though it is not mentioned in any of the Christmas hymns, a word of praise is surely due to the local authorities for not tolerating slum conditions by allowing a family to live in a stable, and though again this is not recorded, no doubt the family got a nice little house near the Nile, with a pleasing view of the Pyramids.

So I will pass the plate round at the party and make a collection for the Freedom from Hunger Campaign, but somehow even that does not quite satisfy me. It's the baby again; I can't get him out of my mind, because what the Bible says about this baby is that when his mother fed, washed and clothed him, she saw God, and that when first the Shepherds, and later the Wise Men with their gifts, knelt at his crib, they saw God.

'There may be other words for other worlds, but for this world the word of God is Christ', and later on as he grew up through boyhood to the stature of a man, he was, in the way he thought and spoke and acted, the perfect expression of God.

'No man,' says an old writer, 'hath seen God at any time', and so all I've got on Christmas Day is the baby in the stable, weak and powerless, subject to suffering, emptied of everything except his babyhood, and in his case not wanted in the world. He had to depend on the adaptability of a cow to move up to give him space to be born. He had to borrow a manger to sleep in, and a cross to die on. But though so small, there was one thing he created, and that was an atmosphere of love wherever he was, not the sloppy, sentimental masquerade which so often people think to be love, but that thing which made men and women live and die for him. The gospel is full of this love, and it began on Christmas Day.

from

The Blacksmith's Daughter

SUSAN OLDACRE

In 1985 when Susan Oldacre came across the diaries of Ann Staight, the daughter of a Victorian village blacksmith

who lived in the Vale of Evesham, she was so moved that she used them as the basis for a fascinating biography. At the time when Ann was writing in her diary about the Christmas of 1882, which is recalled here, she was twenty-seven, only ten years before her tragic and untimely death. In these extracts she mentions her brothers Joe (the village butcher), Tom and John, her sister Sarah, her father Charles, and Joe's wife, Louie. She also refers to Mrs Biscoe and her daughter Annie, close family friends who ran a public house in Enfield. It was here, during an extended holiday, that Ann Staight helped out as a barmaid.

Preparations for Christmas were, unlike now, contained within the few days preceding Christmas Day.

Monday Dec 18. Sis went up to Joe's to see the large beast they killed yesterday.

Inspecting animal carcases may not sound too Christmassy, but 'the large beast' would supply Christmas meals for Joe's customers. Free beef for the tenants from the Hall was an expected, and welcome part of Christmas. On St Thomas's Day (21 December), there were more preparations. The church bells rang early: they *stopped* at 5.30 a.m.! Sarah had been inveigled by Mrs Willougby Jones into decorating the church for Christmas, and after examining the windows for which she would be responsible, she set off into the shrubbery to collect the traditional evergreens, yew, ivy, laurel and holly.

The front room, not much used except for Sunday singing round the piano, was prepared: Tom swept out the chimney and the four 'children' carried the carpet outside for a good

beating. Ann's mother grated nutmegs, cut peel and stoned plums for her Christmas puddings, though traditionally plum puddings were made earlier than this. Stir Up Sunday at the end of November is so called because its Collect (the 25th Sunday after Trinity) begins 'Stir up, we beseech thee, O Lord', and also because it was the time just before Advent to stir the Christmas puddings.

Ann rode with Tom and John to Evesham in Joe's trap to greet the Biscoes. 'Mrs B and Annie came safely, former looking very sadly, but Annie better. We took the luggage to Railway Hotel then went into the town shopping. Annie went with Tom to buy his overcoat. Tom called in at Mr Morris's to try to get calves' feet for Joe, but they had none.' It was nearly dark when they reached home at half past five.

It was Mrs Biscoe's first Christmas without her husband, and a sad one for her, but she and Annie helped Sarah with her 'church work' and she was generous with gifts: 'Mrs B gave me a sweet pretty gold watch and chain, and to Sis she gave a lovely bracelet, and Annie gave us a dear little bracelet each from Mrs Young.' Annie also gave Ann a photograph of 'her dear old home'.

Numerous Christmas cards were dispatched, many to Enfield. Christmas Eve fell on a Sunday that year, and after church 'poor Mrs Biscoe very low and sad, so when we came out we went through shady walk, and down road; she soon felt better.' Ann and Annie made pikelets for tea, and there was a musical evening with Joe and Louie, Leslie and Cormell (Leslie Legge and Cormell Morris were friends). 'We had a nice lot of music. Annie sang some of her Sacred Songs. CM and LL went before 10, the others soon after. Mrs B and us three girls sat talking till nearly 12, after the rest were in bed. Heard the bells ring out the midnight peal.'

· A Worcestershire Christmas ·

Xmas Day, Dec 25th, 1882 . . . Father and boys busy
making toast and ale, and Mother and Sis seeing to the
cooking. Annie and I went to church with the men folks.

> O come all ye faithful
> Joyful and triumphant . . .

In *Silas Marner* George Eliot has described a Christmas
morning very similar to this one: 'The church was fuller than
all through the rest of the year, with red faces among the
abundant dark-green boughs – faces prepared for a longer
service than usual by an odorous breakfast of toast and ale.
Those green boughs, the hymn and the anthem never heard
but at Christmas – even the Athanasian Creed – brought a
vague exulting sense . . .'

Even on Christmas Day there was a postal delivery, with
cards for both girls. Joe and Louie and their friend Alf
Goodall, another butcher, arrived for Christmas lunch of hare
and sirloin beef.

We had dinner rather late. Gave Mrs D's maid her
dinner, Mrs D (Mrs Dunn, an invalid neighbour) had
hers from Rectory. After we had cleared (Sis made fire in
parlour), us girls washed and dressed and put on our best.
Sis and I wore our jewellery presents (Annie gave us a pair
of mittens each, and to the boys she gave two pretty
boxes of matches). Annie helped us get tea, all the 'boys'
went up to Joe's to see after the cattle before tea; Louie,
Alf, Sis, Tom and John went to church, Father went with
Joe to his house. Annie and I washed up and cleared
away, then came upstairs and she read 'The Letters' to
me. LL came before the others were back . . . Later on
the mummers came, and we had them in the kitchen to
act. I did some writing in D. (diary) the while . . .

And after the mummers, the local band! On Boxing Day morning the 'Toddington band came, and played several tunes. Annie and John had a dance or two, I tried, and Alf and Sis.' There was much music, to Ann's delight. Annie gave her, and occasionally John, long music lessons. They were, after all, a sizeable group of musicians – Ann, Annie, John and Louie all played the piano (Charles sometimes played, but from Ann's comment on another occasion, not very well). In addition, Tom, Annie and Louie sang solos, and all joined in singing the hymns and songs.

New Year's Eve 1882 was a Sunday, as Christmas Eve had been. Ann and Annie went to church with the boys, where they listened to a sermon on a text familiar from the funerals they had attended: 'So teach us to number our days' (Psalm 90:12).

> Annie played and sang till supper-time . . . then us two went aloft and did a lot of talking, and I wrote a bit. Boys came up for bed, and pushed in to see what we were doing, and we had a rare 'scrimmage' and shouting. They tried to get at desk, but Sis came to the rescue, and we beat them. Father and Mother followed the boys to bed; us four sat up and read till the bells began ringing Old Year out and New One in. Some men came to the back door wishing us Happy New Year, but we put out the light till they were gone, then went to bed after drinking healths and exchanging good wishes.

1882 had been a year of sharp contrast. It had begun with Ann a barmaid in a busy town close to London; it ended with her sequestered again in a small village remote from any city. Despite the sadnesses of the year, it had been a happy and healthy one for Ann and her family, and it ended in an ideal way: Christmas spent among family and friends.

from

The Archers

JOCK GALLAGHER

The BBC's long-running radio serial The Archers, *the everyday story of countryfolk based on real-life Worcestershire, has not only become a national institution, but has spawned a wide variety of books. Among these is Jock Gallagher's* Archers *trilogy comprising* To the Victor the Spoils, Return to Ambridge *and* Borchester Echoes, *which together recall the family's story since the First World War, covering a period which helped to shape the later fortunes of the small Borsetshire village on which the radio serial is based. The episode related here takes place shortly after the armistice. Phoebe Archer's sons Daniel and Ben have returned home from the war, and Daniel is preparing to take over the running of the family farm following the death of his father. But there's a problem: both Daniel and Ben have designs on the same girl, Doris Forrest, daughter of the local gamekeeper. It takes a Christmas party to bring things to a head.*

Like the three wise men following the star, Phoebe Archer and her two sons wound their way across the fields towards the happy sounds of Christmas celebrations coming from the gamekeeper's lodge on the Winstanley estate. It was a lovely,

26

starlit night and, with a sharp frost making the ground underfoot rock hard, they'd decided to take the short cut rather than walk around by the road.

Everything looked sharp and clear in the eerie light of the moon, and their feet crunched on the frozen grass. The leafless trees were outlined in silver hoar. In the distance the gentle slope of Lakey Hill could be clearly seen as they paused to watch a small animal streak across the silver ground.

There were lamps at every window of the house, and even at two hundred yards they could hear the deep bass voice of William Forrest leading his family and friends in a lusty rendering of 'Oh Come, All Ye Faithful'. Another group was approaching by the pathway from the road, but the Archers couldn't make out who they were.

'He's got the timing right.'

'What do you mean, Ben?'

'Oh come, all ye faithful . . . we're coming!'

Phoebe smiled at her son. It was so good to have him home. He was always making her laugh with his little comments.

'It's a pity we're farmers and not shepherds. Then we could have brought the Forrests some gold and frankincense and myrrh.'

Even Daniel laughed.

'Silly beggar! It was the three wise men who brought gifts, not the shepherds.'

'Yes, of course . . . the shepherds were probably typically tight-fisted. Still, I expect the Forrests will be satisfied with our little Christmas gifts.'

All three of them laughed. When they knocked on the door they were welcomed by William Forrest himself, looking slightly uncomfortable in his Sunday suit.

'You're just in time to join in the carol-singing, and then Lisa will get us all a bite to eat.'

In the parlour the Forrests had already been joined by

several other families, and the big, comfortable room was crowded and noisy. Ben was still in jocular mood.

'Looks like half the village are here, Mr Forrest. I hope it's the right half!'

'Aye, young Ben. We always have the right folk in our house at Christmastime. See you behave yourself!'

William Forrest was very proud of what had become one of the traditions of the Ambridge Christmas. As a gamekeeper he needed to carry some authority, and one of the ways he had tried to do that was to make himself and Lisa prominent in the life of the village. It had been hard going at first because there was a natural suspicion of gamekeepers, and Lisa, who had been in service as a scullery maid, was very shy. However, they had both persevered and had succeeded. This was their sixteenth Christmas party, and over the last ten years, at least, no one had been known to refuse an invitation. Everyone who regarded themselves as anyone was there this evening. No wonder William bade Ben Archer to behave himself.

Ben had been trying to spot Doris, but she wasn't in the room. He did, however, see Sally Blower and she was a very good substitute . . . nearly as pretty, a bit older and a bit more experienced. With a wink at his elder brother, he eased his way through the noisy crowd towards her.

'Hello, Sally. I haven't seen you in years. Are you still working in Borchester?'

Before she could reply, Mr Forrest announced that the next carol would be 'While Shepherds Watched Their Flocks By Night'. Further conversation was impossible, so Ben slipped his arm round Sally's shoulders and they both joined happily in the singing.

More persevering than his young brother, Daniel Archer found Doris in the kitchen, where she was helping her mother cut a great pile of sandwiches and cold meats.

'Evening, Mrs Forrest . . . Doris. Happy Christmas to you both.'

'Daniel Archer . . . it's lovely to see you. I'm glad you were able to tear yourself away from Brookfield for five minutes. Here, would you mind giving our Doris a hand while I go and check that there's plenty of mulled ale left?'

'Oh, aye. I suppose so.'

Daniel was surprised to have such an early opportunity to talk to Doris, and now that it had come he wasn't so sure it was a good idea. He felt a bit flustered.

'What do you want me to do, Doris? I'm not very good at cutting bread.'

'Well you can't stand there looking like a great awkward lump. Try putting the sandwiches on to plates.'

Awkward was precisely how he felt . . . but not about the bread. He was too worried about the exact words he should use without making a fool of himself. It should have been so easy. He'd practised it often enough in his mind.

'Doris . . .'

'Yes, Daniel?'

All the carefully considered preamble disappeared from his head.

'Doris, do you see us as sweethearts?'

There was a great thump and the kitchen door flew open. Mrs Forrest came back carrying two empty jugs.

'The ale's fine, so off you go Daniel. The kitchen's no place for a man. You can go too, Doris. I'll finish these things off myself. Thank you for your help, Daniel.'

The opportunity gone, his question unanswered except by a shy non-committal smile, Daniel Archer reluctantly pushed his way back into the crowded parlour. Doris followed him. They were just in time to hear Mr Forrest declare that it was time for 'party pieces'. Everyone groaned in mock despair. Some of the solo performances were already well known around

the district and their highly variable standards only added to
the amusement.

Usually, it was Mr Forrest who began this part of the
evening with a quite tuneful rendition of an old local song
called 'The Village Pump'. But instead of standing up to sing,
he announced that he had a special surprise up his sleeve.

'Young Tom has been practising his performance for some
weeks now and I reckon that such dedication deserves special
attention. If none of you minds, I'll ask him to get things
going for us tonight.'

Little Tom Forrest shuffled forward, looking very nervous.
His elder brother Teddy covered his face with his hands and
groaned loudly, but everyone else tried to encourage him.

'What are you going to do, Tommy? Recite?'

'Sing? What are you going to sing?'

'I'm going to sing "The Village Pump".'

There was a great roar of laughter, which the poor lad didn't
understand. He didn't know his father had been singing the
same song for as long as anyone could remember, nor that it
was now always met with friendly derision. Undaunted, he
ploughed on and sang every single verse and was rewarded by
great cheers when he had finished.

As the evening's entertainment unfolded, Doris found
herself being pursued by both the Archer brothers. It was all
very flattering, but she was beginning to get a bit worried. She
had known that Daniel had been about to get quite serious in
the kitchen, and she had been relieved when her mother had
interrupted them. At eighteen she felt she was still too young
to get serious about anyone . . . although at the same time she
didn't want to say anything that might make Daniel go away.

Nothing, though, would make Ben go away, it seemed. He
had appeared very interested in Sally Blower when Doris had
first spotted him – at least, they were involved in a long
conversation, and she'd felt she was interrupting something

when she'd gone to have a word with Sally. Since then, however, Ben had tried to persuade Doris to stand under the large bunch of mistletoe hanging from the centre of the ceiling about half a dozen times, and she wasn't sure how many more times she'd be able to fend him off. It was thinking about how to keep him at bay that finally made up her mind for her. She realised that she preferred Daniel Archer!

Unaware of this development, Daniel was becoming increasingly uncomfortable. He was quite shy and didn't mix very well, and it was hard work trying to keep up a conversation without going on and on about the problems of running Brookfield Farm. He reckoned people must be bored with all his worries. Since Lisa Forrest had thrown him out of the kitchen, his attempts to have another word with Doris had all been thwarted. Several times it was his own brother who interrupted them. Was he being mischievous or was he, too, serious about Doris? He'd have to tackle him about it at some point.

At eleven o'clock the party began to break up. Most of the menfolk present had to be up at the crack of dawn, and after the plentiful supplies of mulled ale they'd supped, they would need a good few hours of sleep.

Daniel was helping his mother to find her shawl when he saw Ben trap Doris under the bunch of mistletoe. He had his arms wrapped tightly around her and was kissing her full on the lips.

Sensing the anger mounting in her eldest son, Phoebe decided to intervene.

'Come on, Ben. We have to be going home now. We must let Mr Forrest get to his bed.'

It had little effect. Ben continued to kiss Doris as the others in the room laughed nervously. Daniel didn't laugh at all. He watched grim-faced until he could bear it no longer.

'Right, Ben. That's more than enough. Leave the lass alone. Let her breathe for heaven's sake.'

31

'Sorry, Doris. No harm meant. I thought you and I had a bit of an understanding. If I was wrong, I apologise.'

Doris smiled in relief. Her father, only half aware of what had happened, put his arm around her shoulders protectively.

With only the barest of polite farewells to Mr and Mrs Forrest, Daniel strode out into the night, leaving his mother to do a proper job of thanking them for their hospitality. Halfway across the frost-covered fields, he realised his brother was still back at the lodge. He wanted to go back to make sure he wasn't still pestering Doris, but he knew he couldn't do that without making everyone even more embarrassed.

When he got home to Brookfield, Daniel was still angry. Uncharacteristically, he banged about the farmhouse, nearly knocking over one of the lamps. He went to his room and lay down on the bed fully clothed. Somehow he reckoned that he wasn't going to sleep very well.

Lying there with his stomach churning, he heard the others come back. After a few minutes he listened as his mother came quietly up the stairs and went to bed. Downstairs, his brother moved noisily about the kitchen. Glancing at the clock in the corner of the room as he leaned across to put out the lamp, Daniel saw that there was still a quarter of an hour left of Christmas Day.

As the last minutes of Christmas Day ticked away, neither brother slept, and the early hours of that Boxing Day morning found the increasingly bitter feud developing, to the point where Daniel and Ben were locked in a vicious and bloody fight which became a watershed in the annals of Archers' history.

from

The Season of the Year

JOHN MOORE

The vision of the English countryside evoked by the works of John Moore has brought pleasure to many people. He lived from 1907 to 1967 and wrote extensively about the rural borderland of Worcestershire and Gloucestershire which he knew so well, and on which he based his famous Brensham Trilogy. *He was living in Bredon when, in 1954, he wrote* The Season of the Year, *his month-by-month commentary on country life, from which this first seasonal offering of his writings is taken.*

Christmas, of course, is never what it was. We are reminded of this fact every year by old Jeremy Skinner, whose memory goes back seventy years or so and who sadly shakes his head as the landlord brings in holly-sprigs to decorate his bar.

'In the old days,' says Jeremy, 'there was *real* berries on the holly, not just a little pip here and there. You could scarce see the leaves for red berries. That was because winters were harder then. Nature provided the berries as food for the birds.'

Always on Christmas Eve he pulls out of his pocket, and

33

The Worcestershire countryside in winter, a scene typical of
those on which John Moore based his inspirational writing

passes round the company in the bar, a very faded yellowing
photograph in which he takes pleasure and pride. It represents
a butcher's shop in the nearby town, and bears on its back the
inscription, 'Christmas 1913'. If you look carefully – and
Jeremy will insist that you do – you will make out, as it were
through the mists of time, an array of enormous sides of beef, a
dozen at least hanging from their hooks, with innumerable
legs of mutton and loins of pork. Among them stands the
proud butcher in his striped apron; at least Jeremy assures you
it is the butcher, though his huge hands are like lumps of beef
and his broad features peering between the haunches are liable
to be confused with a boar's head.

'Look at it,' says Jeremy grimly. 'Just look. I simply ask you to look, that's all.'

We look.

'The rosettes,' says Jeremy, 'you can just see 'em up there in the left-hand corner, were worn by the prize-winning beasts at the Christmas Fat Stock Fair. Never bought anything but the best, he didn't. His sirloins would melt in your mouth. When I looked at my Christmas joint – if you call it a joint – this evening, and when I thought of those sirloins, well . . . believe it or not, but I minds the time when my old mother, and she was a hale and hearty woman, couldn't lift down our Christmas joint out of the larder; and "Jeremy", she called, "Jeremy me boy, just come here and give us a hand. . . ."'

You would think, to listen to Jeremy, that Father Christmas had become a tattered beggar dressed in rags, that he who was once fat and prosperous and prodigal was now a pale starving waif. And perhaps there would be some truth in this sad picture if the festival were simply a matter of beef and booze; instead of being a mood, a spirit, a leaven, something imponderable, a high wind blowing through our hearts. It is much more profound a mystery, fortunately, than the sirloins and the fat butcher in Jeremy's photograph; although even they are becoming a trifle mysterious as our memories fade and the photograph fades and the too, too solid flesh melts into a peasoup fog.

'There,' says Jeremy, pointing at the bottom left-hand corner with an old gnarled finger, 'that was snow.'

And indeed the photograph is flecked all over with white spots which we thought were due to its great age.

'Snow,' repeats Jeremy firmly. 'When that photo was took, it was snowing. And it went on snowing for a week. None of your new-fangled green Christmases then! It snowed for a week and, on Christmas Day, after church, we sat in here at noon drinking our beer by candlelight. Why by candlelight?

Because the drifts was above the winders of the bar, see. Drink our beer by candlelight we did, and when I say beer I mean beer, not this belly-chilling stuff we get today. . . .'

Elgar and Christmas – 1

Apart from his gifts as a composer of great music, Sir Edward Elgar also enjoyed writing verse, which he would often interpose in letters and greetings to friends and relatives. At Christmas in 1927, he was living at Battenhall Manor on the outskirts of Worcester and had invited his daughter Carice – who was suffering from an eye infection – and her husband, Henry Blake, to spend what proved to be a cold and snowy festive season with him. His gifts to them that year – a pin-brooch and some pine-scented body lotion – were each accompanied by one of his inimitable verses.

'To Clarice on Christmas Day, 1927,
with a PIN of some Price.'

This day, whate'er the Fates decree,
Shall still be kept with Joy by me;
This day then, let us not be told
Your eye is bad, and I am old,

Nor think on mere fantasmic Ills,
Nor talk of Spectacles and Pills;
Tomorrow will be time enough
To hear such edifying Stuff.

Yet, since some Reason must be sought
For better and more pleasing Thought,
Although this reason's plaguy thin,
Accept on Christmas Day a PIN!

'To Henry Blake on Christmas Day, 1927,
with a Pleasant Mess of Pine Unguents.'

Resolved a festive verse to pay
To Henry Blake on Christmas Day;
Furnished with Paper, Pen and Ink
I gravely sat me down to think!

Sir Edward Elgar: a penchant for cryptic verse

· A Worcestershire Christmas ·

Worcester Cathedral, long associated with Elgar's music.
This photograph was taken in the 1920s when the composer
was living in the city, and before the cathedral tower lost
its decorative pinnacles

I bit my Pen, and racked my Head,
But found my Wit & Fancy Fled.

Failing a Verse, I Unguents found
To keep the Epidermis sound.

A Small Boy's Christmas

FRED ARCHER

This second dip into the treasure-chest of Fred Archer's early memories of rural life in the Vale of Evesham, provides a nostalgic account of Christmastime when he was a schoolboy.

We didn't start to think about Christmas when I was a small boy at prep school until nearing the end of the term. We used to break up about a week before the festival, with blancmange and cake for tea, and crackers and tinsel decorating the classroom. Then I came home in the early evening on the seven o'clock train – the last train on the branch line from Evesham.

It was cosy in the barn on those short winter days towards the end of December. I liked to creep in and watch the cows being milked by Fred the cowman, who sat on a three-legged stool with his head covered by a greasy cap worn backwards. A hurricane lamp slung on a broken plough trace gave a little light for the milking at five o'clock.

The hens, perched in rows on the tall hayloader, cackled occasionally when Fred walked with his three-gallon bucket and poured the warm creamy milk into a shining five-gallon container. There is a strange comforting feeling for man and boy to be with cattle tied up to the manger on a winter's night;

39

the incessant cud chewing, the look in the cows' placid eyes.

Next morning Fred and Dad caught the Christmas cockerels one by one under the thatch in an old bull pen. As they were killed I walked with Fred and he hung them up on hooks and nails from the whitewashed ceiling of the back kitchen.

That week I'd already spent one day by the parish quarry on Bredon Hill with Dad, a neighbour and my brother Tom, ferreting the holts for rabbits. Dad was what was known as a Guardian of the Poor and he and his partner gave rabbits to Evesham Workhouse every Christmas to enable people called inmates (who I prefer to call patients) to have a rabbit pie supper.

Christmas drew near. In those days the season seemed more of a festival, more acute, when everything was to happen in a few short days. In the window of the village shop – a shop and

An Ashton-under-Hill villager with rabbits caught on
Bredon Hill during Christmas week. They were destined for
the festive rabbit pies served to the inmates of Evesham
Workhouse

40

post office combined — I saw boxes of chocolates wrapped in fancy paper with Father Christmas decorating the pink ribbons, dishes of muscatels and almonds, sugar mice and Christmas cards. Standing outside by the door was a Christmas tree in half a nine-gallon barrel. And when I went to post letters or buy stamps, I would watch parcels being weighed on shining brass scales. There would have been similar scenes in the other villages encircling Bredon Hill.

At my prep school Miss Morris had taught us poems about Christmas. We sang 'Who is He in Yonder Stall?' among other carols. I liked the story of the manger. It was so much like Fred the cowman and his milking stool. Nothing has changed, I thought. The shepherd still watched his flock by night, but he watched the ewes in the lambing pen too.

Miss Morris always impressed me when she read to us Thomas Hardy's poem 'The Oxen':

> Christmas Eve and twelve of the clock.
> 'Now they are all on their knees,'
> An elder said as we sat in a flock
> By the embers in hearthside ease.
>
> We pictured the meek mild creatures where
> They dwelt in their strawy pen,
> Nor did it occur to one of us there
> To doubt they were kneeling then.
>
> So fair a fancy few would weave
> In these years! Yet, I feel,
> If someone said on Christmas Eve,
> 'Come; see the Oxen kneel!
>
> 'In the lonely barton by yonder coomb,
> Our childhood used to know.'
> I should go with him in the gloom,
> Hoping it might be so.

· A Worcestershire Christmas ·

In our world today when things have to be seen and to have an explanation before they can be believed, the mystery of Christmas is unique. Santa Claus conjures up so much in a child's mind, while the 'good news' still comes through as a light to cheer the dark days.

Do the oxen kneel on Christmas Eve? As a boy I crept out one Christmas Eve at twelve o'clock to find out. In the cattle shed, four oxen and two heifers were chained to a manger. You may have noticed that cattle kneel first when they lie down. The oxen were lying in the straw and their fore feet were doubled under their briskets in a kneeling position. Taking the candle lantern back to the house, I was satisfied.

On Christmas Day our house was decorated with holly, ivy and mistletoe. Every picture was festooned with greenery, and the old grandfather clock in the hall was hung with holly, while a bough of mistletoe was fixed to a big nail by the front door.

I often think back to those inmates of the Evesham Workhouse enjoying their Christmas rabbit pie, and I am reminded of George Sims who lived from 1847 to 1922. He was a journalist and agitator for social reform, and he wrote 'In the Workhouse, Christmas Day':

> It is Christmas Day in the workhouse
> And the cold bare walls are bright
> With garlands of green and holly
> And the place is a pleasant sight.
>
> For with clean washed hands and faces,
> In a long and hungry line
> The paupers sit at the tables,
> For this is their hour to dine.
>
> And the guardians and their ladies,
> Although the wind is east,

Have come in their furs and wrappers
To watch their charges feast.

To smile and be condescending,
Put puddings on paper plates.
To be hosts at the workhouse banquet
They've paid for — with the rates.

That I'm afraid was the scene many years ago. I wonder sometimes whether the extra food at Christmas did compensate a little for the hard rations throughout the year. In those times, perhaps the condescension of their so-called 'betters' was hard to bear, but I went to one rabbit pie supper when the workhouse was called by another name — the Public Assistance Institution. It was good to see the beam on some of the faces I knew.

A snowy winter at Elmley Castle, one of the Bredon Hill villages which figure in Fred Archer's seasonal reminiscences

A Robin at Christmas

GEOFFREY NELSON

Dr Geoffrey Nelson has worked extensively in support of the Worcestershire Nature Conservation Trust and is a knowledgeable writer on the county's flora and fauna. In 1989 he penned these seasonal thoughts about one of our favourite birds.

The robin redbreast, which has appeared so frequently on Christmas cards since they were introduced in Victorian times, has come to symbolise the very spirit of Christmas.

Its popularity at this time of year may, in part, be explained by the fact that it can often be heard singing its cheerful tune and displaying its bright red breast even on the coldest and dullest of winter days. Another reason is the robin's religious significance which can be traced back to an early legend.

According to the story the robin was originally a dull brown bird, until the day of the crucifixion when it took pity on Christ and, picking thorns from his crown, stained its breast with blood. Since that day all adult robins have had a red breast.

This has led to a superstition that it is unlucky to harm a robin, a notion that was repeated by the poet, William Blake:

The robin and the wren
Are God Almighty's cock and hen.
Him who harries their nest
Never shall his soul have rest.

In this verse Blake fell into the common error of his time – the belief that the wren was a female robin.

The robin is a particular favourite in this country, frequently visiting our gardens and bird tables. As most gardeners will know, a robin will often arrive as soon as they start digging, and search in the newly turned soil for worms and insects. They are so friendly and self-confident that they will sometimes alight on your fork and even take food from your hand.

In this respect the British robin is unique, for continental robins, which are of the same species, are more timid birds living in woods and seldom venturing into gardens. It has

'The robin has come to symbolise the very spirit of Christmas'

45

been suggested that the difference in behaviour between British and continental birds is the result of the attitude of humans. On the continent, robins, like other small birds, are killed for food, whereas in Britain the robin has been treated with affection for centuries.

It is less easy to explain why the British have for so long had this affectionate relationship with the bird. The male robin is a pugnacious little creature which marks out and defends his territory against all other robins throughout the year. His song is a demonstration of his ownership and an announcement of his territorial rights. It is a challenge to invaders.

A male entering the territory of another male is immediately challenged. If it ignores the warning, a fight will ensue, and the winner will occupy the territory.

In December the males are establishing their territories, and early in January they begin to pair off. The female, or hen, will enter the territory of the male and, ignoring his threats, attempt to stay. As a result of her behaviour he may come to recognise her as a potential mate and over a period of time a pair-bond relationship develops. This may take some weeks, but eventually the female starts to gather materials for a nest. As she builds the nest the male begins to feed her, a process that continues right through to the time she hatches the eggs.

The hen normally builds her nest in a hollow in the ground. It is constructed of moss and dead leaves and lined with hair. Robins do, however, have a reputation for nesting in the most unlikely places, such as letter-boxes, jam jars and old boots. There is one story of a robin that built her nest in one morning between 9 o'clock and noon in the pocket of a coat hung up in a garden shed. Another account tells of a robin which nested on the engine of a car, the owner of which was unable to use the vehicle until the brood had been reared!

The young birds do not have red breasts, but are speckled brown, resembling thrushes, to which family the robins belong. A pair of robins will raise two broods of five or six youngsters each year, but because of predators and bad weather only one is likely to survive to breed in the following year.

In the same period it is likely that one of the original pair will also have died. In this way the population remains roughly the same, except that the death rate increases in hard winters.

If we are to maintain our population of robins it is helpful to put out food and drink, not only at Christmas but throughout the winter.

from

The Adventures of Mr Verdant Green

CUTHBERT BEDE

Cuthbert Bede was the pseudonym of the Reverend Edward Bradley, a one-time curate in Kidderminster, who died in 1889 aged sixty-two. He was a gifted writer, and his fictional account of Mr Verdant Green's protracted, and often humorous, adventures while a university student at Oxford, is a notable example of literary Victoriana. In these extracts, Verdant Green the undergraduate is spending the

· A Worcestershire Christmas ·

festive season at the family home. It is the end of Christmas week and he has already held a number of memorable celebrations.

Christmas had come; the season of kindness, and hospitality; the season when the streams of benevolence flow full in their channels; the season when the Honourable Miss Hyems indulges herself with ice, while the vulgar Jack Frost regales himself with cold-without. Christmas had come, and had brought with it an old-fashioned winter; and, as Mr Verdant Green stands with his hands in his pockets, and gazes from the drawing-room of his paternal mansion, he looks forth upon a white world.

The snow is everywhere. The shrubs are weighed down by

A self-portrait of Cuthbert Bede, pseudonym of the
Reverend Edward Bradley

masses of it; the terrace is knee-deep in it; the plaster Apollo in the long walk is more than knee-deep in it, and is furnished with a surplice and wig, like a half-blown bishop. The distant country looks the very ghost of a landscape: the white-walled cottages seem part and parcel of the snow-drifts around them – drifts that take every variety of form, and are swept by the wind into faery wreaths, and fantastic caves.

The old mill-wheel is locked fast, and gemmed with giant icicles; its slippery stairs are more slippery than ever. Golden gorse and purple heather are now all out of colour; orchards put forth blossoms of real snow; the gently swelling hills look bright and dazzling in the wintry sun; the grey church tower has grown from grey to white; nothing looks black, except the swarms of rooks that dot the snowy fields, or make their caws to be heard from among the dark branches of the stately elms that form the avenue to the Manor Green.

It is a rare busy time for the intelligent Mr Mole the gardener. He is always sweeping at that avenue, and do what he will, he cannot keep it clear from snow. As Mr Verdant Green looks forth upon the white world, his gaze is more particularly directed to this avenue, as though the form of the intelligent Mr Mole was an object of interest. From time to time Mr Verdant Green consults his watch in a nervous manner, and is utterly indifferent to the appeals of the robin-redbreast who is hopping about outside, in expectation of the dinner which has been daily given to him.

Mr Verdant Green, slightly colouring up, fixes his gaze upon the lodge-gate through which a group of ladies and gentlemen are passing. Stepping back for a moment, and stealing a glance at himself in the mirror, Mr Verdant Green hurriedly arranges and disarranges his hair – pulls about his collar – ties and unties his neck-handkerchief – buttons and then unbuttons his coat – takes another look from the window – and sees the intelligent Mr Mole (besom in hand) salaaming the party.

· A Worcestershire Christmas ·

'Mr Mole (besom in hand) salaaming the party . . .' —
Cuthbert Bede's own illustration of an episode in the story

*As the guests approach up the avenue to the house, we are
introduced to them in turn, and afforded a glimpse of their
participation in Mr Verdant Green's earlier celebrations
during that Christmas week.*

Hale and hearty, the picture of amiability and gentlemanly
feeling, comes the rector, Mr Larkyns, sturdily crunching the
frozen snow, which has defied all the besom powers of the
intelligent Mr Mole. Here, too, is Mr Charles Larkyns, and
moreover, his friend Henry Bouncer, Esq, who has come to
Christmas at the Rectory. Following in their wake is a fourth

gentleman attired in the costume peculiar to clergymen, dissenting ministers, linen-drapers' assistants, and tavern waiters. He happens to belong to the first-named section, and is no less a person than the Rev. Josiah Meek, B.A. (St Christopher's Coll., Oxon) who, for the last three months, has officiated as Mr Larkyns's curate. He appears to be of a peace-loving, lamb-like disposition; and, though sportive as a lamb when occasion requires, is yet of timid ways and manners. He is timid, too, in voice, speaking in a feeble treble; he is timid, too, in his address, more particularly as regards females; and he has mild-looking whiskers that are far too timid to assume any decided or obtrusive colour, and have fallen back on a generalised whitey-brown tint.

With the four gentlemen come two ladies – young ladies, moreover, who as penny-a-liners say, are 'possessed of considerable personal attractions'. These are the Misses Honeywood, the blooming daughters of the rector's only sister; and they have come from the far land of the North, and are looking as fresh and sweet as their own heathery hills. The roses of health that bloom upon their cheeks have been brought into full blow by the keen, sharp breeze; the shepherd's-plaid shawls drawn tightly around them give the outline of figures that gently swell into the luxuriant line of beauty and grace. Altogether, they are damsels who are pleasant to the eye, and very fair to look upon.

Since they last visited their uncle four years had passed, and in that time, they had shot up to womanhood, although they were not yet out of their teens. Their father was a landed proprietor living in north Northumberland.

During the past summer, the rector had taken a trip to Northumberland, in order to see his sister, and refresh himself with a clergyman's fortnight at Honeywood Hall, and he would not leave his sister and her husband until he had extracted from them a promise that they would bring down their two eldest daughters to spend Christmas with him.

This was accordingly agreed to, and, more than that, acted upon; and little Mr Bouncer and his sister Fanny were asked to meet them; but, to relieve the rector of a superfluity of lady guests, Miss Bouncer's quarters had been removed to the Manor Green.

It was quite an event in the history of our hero and his sisters. Four years ago, they, and Kitty and Patty Honeywood, were mere chits, for whom dolls had not altogether lost their interest, and who considered it as promotion when they sat in the drawing-room on company evenings, instead of being shown up at dessert. Four years at this period of life makes a vast change in young ladies, and the Green and Honeywood girls had so altered since last they met, that they had almost needed a fresh introduction to each other. But a day's intimacy made them bosom friends; and the Manor Green soon saw such revels as it had not seen for many a long year.

Every night there were (in the language of the play-bills of provincial theatres) 'singing and dancing, with a variety of other entertainments'; the 'other entertainments' occasionally consisting (as is scandalously affirmed) of a very favourite class of entertainment – popular at all times, but running mad riot at the Christmas season – wherein two performers of either sex take their places beneath a white-berried bough, and go through a species of dance, or *pas de fascination*, accompanied by mysterious rites and solemnities that have been scrupulously observed, and handed down to us from the earliest age.

Mr Verdant Green during the short – alas! too short – Christmas week, had performed more polkas than he had ever danced in his life; and, under the charming tuition of Miss Patty Honeywood, was fast becoming a proficient in the *valse à deux temps*. She was both good-natured and persevering: and she allowed our hero to dance on her feet without a murmur.

It is an old saying that Gratitude begets Love. Mr Verdant

'Mr Verdant Green during the short – alas! too short –
Christmas week, had performed more polkas than he had
ever danced in his life.' Cuthbert Bede produced numerous
drawings such as this to illustrate his book

Green had already reached the first part of this dangerous
creation, for he felt grateful to the pretty Patty for the
good-humoured trouble she bestowed on the awkwardness,
which he now, for the first time, began painfully to perceive.
But, what his gratitude might end in, he had never taken the
trouble to inquire.

It was perhaps ungrateful in our hero to prefer Miss Patty
Honeywood to Miss Fanny Bouncer, especially when the latter
was staying in the house, and had been so warmly recommended

to his notice by her vivacious brother. Especially, too, as there was nothing to be objected to in Miss Bouncer, saving the fact that some might have affirmed she was a trifle too much inclined to *embonpoint*, and was indeed a bouncer in person as well as in name.

But these sort of likings are not made to rule, and Mr Verdant Green could see Miss Fanny Bouncer approach without betraying any of those symptoms of excitement, under the influence of which we had the privilege to see him, as he gazed from the window of his paternal mansion and then, on beholding the approaching form of Miss Patty Honeywood, rush wildly to the vestibule.

The party had no occasion to ring, for the hall door was already opened for them, and Mr Verdant Green was soon exchanging a delightful pressure of the hand with the blooming Patty.

'What a mysterious communication, Verdant!' remarks the rector, as they pass into the house. But the rector is only to be let so far into the secret as to be informed that, at the evening party which is to be held at the Manor Green that night, a charade or two will be acted, in order to diversify the amusements. The Misses Honeywood are great adepts in this sort of pastime; so, also, are Miss Bouncer and her brother. For although the latter does not shine as a mimic, yet, as he is never deserted by his accustomed coolness, he has plenty of the nonchalance and readiness which are a requisite for charade acting. The Misses Honeywood and Mr Bouncer have therefore suggested to Mr Verdant Green and his sisters, that to get up a little amateur performance would be 'great fun'; and the suggetion has met with a warm approval.

So charades were determined on; and, when words had been hunted up, a council of war was called. But, as the ladies and gentlemen hold their council with closed doors, we cannot intrude upon them. We must therefore wait till the evening, when the result of their deliberations will be publicly manifested.

Having planned the evening's festive entertainment with Mr Verdant Green, the guests depart for home to prepare themselves for their return visit a few hours later. For the Manor Green, wrapped in snow in these last hours of the dying year, it was to prove a memorable occasion, and the charades and dancing continued well into the night. At length, as Cuthbert Bede describes, 'the last light is out, and Mr Verdant Green is lying uncomfortably on his back, and is waltzing through Dreamland with the blooming Patty Honeywood'.

Winter

WILLIAM SHENSTONE

The poet William Shenstone was born in Halesowen in 1714 and for much of his life lived at The Leasowes, a stately mansion standing in magnificent landscaped grounds which he created himself and from which it is said he gained considerable inspiration for his writing. Although little evidence of his former home remains and the grounds are now transformed into a modern golf course, his work survives, and this verse, entitled 'Winter', was written in 1746 as the words to a song.

55

· *A Worcestershire Christmas* ·

No more, ye warbling birds! rejoice:
Of all that cheer'd the plain,
Echo alone preserves her voice,
And she – repeats my pain.

Where'er my lovesick limbs I lay
To shun the rushing wind,
Its busy murmurs seem to say,
'She never will be kind!'

The Naiads, o'er their frozen urns,
In icy chains repine;
And each in sullen silence mourns
Her freedom lost, like mine!

Soon will the sun's returning rays
The cheerless frost control;
When will relenting Delia chase
The winter of my soul?

from

Swings and
Roundabouts

GRAHAM DILLEY

*In 1987 the charismatic Worcestershire cricketer Graham
Dilley wrote an entertaining autobiographical account of
his career, in conjunction with cricket correspondent and
journalist Graham Otway. In it he tells of his controver-
sial cricketing life as a Worcestershire, Kent and England
bowler, and one of the most memorable episodes deals with
the tour to Australia in the winter of 1986/87, during
which Christmas was celebrated in what was certainly a
less than traditional manner.*

The knee was still playing up when we arrived in Tasmania for
the final state fixture of the winter, and since it was not a vital
match for me the tour selectors and I agreed that rest would be
the safest bet. We all had three strenuous weeks ahead of us
with the Melbourne Test starting on Boxing Day, the
America's Cup Perth Challenge opening the New Year and the
Sydney Test soon after that, so there was no point in risking
more serious damage. . . .

Our overnight trip to Canberra two days before Christmas

to play against an eleven raised by Australia's cricket-mad Prime Minister Bob Hawke took on far more significance than the tour planners could have possibly foreseen. Instead of enjoying a leisurely day out in Australia's administrative capital, the fifty-over contest proved to be a fitness test for both Ian Botham and myself. Botham had not played since breaking down at Perth and although he only bowled off eight paces, his ten overs for 42 runs, with two wickets, was sufficient to suggest he had a role to play in the forthcoming Test at Melbourne. I fired in six overs straight off with the new ball, but my knee did not feel comfortable, my line was all askew and suddenly there were doubts about whether I would be available.

Whatever my troubles there was no way I was going to allow them to spoil the festive season at the Menzies Hotel in Melbourne. Guests visiting there for the first time are prone to think they are in somewhere like Pentonville or Wandsworth, since the interior is built like a prison – two long high blocks of rooms, each with a balcony, facing each other, with a glass roof and a long drop down into the bar area below.

Foreboding it may have looked but the whole tour party was in high spirits; although we were still only one-nil up in the Test series, there was general feeling that after our performances in Perth and Adelaide there was no way the Australians were going to beat us. We were all aware there was a test due to start on Boxing Day, and that called for restraint on the booze front but it failed to stop us enjoying ourselves.

Ian Botham opened up his suite to all the players on Christmas Eve and with Elton John in attendance we had quite a lively party. Although we were all careful not to go overboard in the drinks stakes I have to confess to suffering from a slight headache when I awoke on Christmas morning and hardly felt up to attending the traditional champagne party thrown by the press. After a couple of glasses of bubbly,

· *A Worcestershire Christmas* ·

Worcestershire and England bowler Graham Dilley, whose
Christmas celebrations during England's 1986/87 tour of
Australia, were anything but traditional

however, I was put in the right frame of mind for the rest of
the day by a pantomime acted out by the reporters.

It was a tribute to the way Peter Lush had fostered relations
between the press and the players throughout the tour that we
all found their act pretty amusing. Their chosen subject for the
ten-minute drama was Mike Gatting's highly publicised
sleep-in on the first morning of our game with Victoria in
Melbourne. Titled 'The Big Sleep' it portrayed Mike, played
by Dave Norrie of the *News of the World*, lying in bed
surrounded by mounds of room service trays covered in food,
having a nightmare about the possibility of David Gower
regaining the England captaincy.

Anyone can oversleep on tour, particularly with an itinerary

as gruelling as ours was, but it was not quite what the people at Lord's expect from an England captain. Still, Gatting had weathered the storm a fortnight earlier and the mood was right, the time was right and the amount of mickey-taking just right for the pantomime to be well received – even Botham was in stitches when the room service waiter said his next order was to deliver some coke to the 'greatest living cricketer'.

As the press party broke up Phillip DeFreitas and I returned to our room to prepare for the second traditional event of Christmas Day, the players' fancy dress lunch. On previous overseas trips they had always been exclusively male affairs with wives and girlfriends forced to eat elsewhere so that any player who had chosen not to bring his partner out to join him on tour would not feel he was missing out and become depressed. The rules, however, had changed in the three years since I had last toured, and the ladies' presence made very little difference, although the humour and language had to be toned down to allow for the presence of children.

As elected secretary of the grandly titled 'Players' Social Committee' I had been fairly deeply involved in the organisation of the party. My main task in the previous weeks had been to prepare charges for the Kangaroo Courts which had sat regularly to charge and fine players for ridiculous misdemeanours to raise money for the lunch. Players had been hauled before the committee for the most trivial of offences but such was the justice of the proceedings that the more minor the charges, the bigger they were blown out of proportion, and the fines were adjusted accordingly. Some examples of the hearings can never be released to the public, but of the others, physio Laurie Brown was done for ringing home and speaking to himself on his answering machine, DeFreitas was fined for referring to the Australian Premier Bob Hawke as Bob Hope, while our overweight manager Peter Lush was frequently chided for claiming that he had actually passed the pre-tour medical.

The hefty amount of cash raised by the courts was all put towards the presents which the social committee had decided each player should receive at the lunch. Again some of the best examples are team secrets, but Botham received a packet of grass seed, John Emburey a pair of underpants shaped for an elephant, while my colleagues had decided I should receive an emergency cigarette held in a glass box for use only when I ran out of the free supply laid on by Benson and Hedges, our official sponsors in Australia.

Some of the fancy dress costumes were simply outrageous and highly imaginative. Although a lot of hard work went into their conception after the social committee had given each player a specific letter of the alphabet which had to be worked into a theme, finding the right gear in Australia with dress hire shops in almost every city was not as taxing a problem as it is, say, in India. My own plan was to get myself wheeled into the lunch on a stretcher with an intravenous drip of Bollinger champagne to imitate the famous laid back attitude of David Gower. Sadly the plan backfired since obtaining a stretcher proved a tough task and I ended up being pushed on a porter's trolley.

DeFreitas walked away with first prize after turning up as Diana Ross complete with a long dark wig and clinging long red dress. In fact before he was even seen in public we tried to get him to shave off his moustache and planned to tell Wilf Slack that Ms Ross was in the bar downstairs waiting to share a Christmas drink. Unfortunately DeFreitas would not play ball to that extent though from the back he looked just the part.

As the party came to a close we all drifted back to our rooms for a quick snooze, but even though there was an important Test due to start within twenty-four hours, we still had one other item on the agenda. The BBC had arranged through the

Noel Edmonds' Show for us all to be linked up with our folks back home. Although I had particularly been looking forward to seeing Helen, the whole thing was a complete disaster from start to finish. In agreeing to take part Peter Lush had insisted that we be included in the first part of the show so that we could all get off to bed, but we were kept hanging around for an hour and were unable to get away from the cameras until 11.15 p.m. Furthermore the sound and picture quality on the tiny monitors in front of us were so bad that the whole event turned into a farce. It was then that Lush demonstrated how there was no way during the tour that people were going to use his players and get away with it. After two fairly heavy days celebrating Christmas he knew that we all needed to retire early and he wrote a strong letter of complaint to the BBC on our behalf.

As Boxing Day dawned and we all went early to the ground for practice there was still a lingering doubt over my knee. Although the fluid had subsided, Laurie Brown had discovered that I had damaged a ligament and felt I should take a late fitness test. It was a tough decision to make when Gatting came up and asked me whether I could play or not. In such cases I had always believed in honesty being the best policy and I told him that while I might have been able to start the match there was no guarantee that after three or four days I would still be able to bowl. Some of the other lads moaned a bit when I pulled out, but in my own mind I was prepared to take their criticism and let someone else who was fully fit have my place – it was going to be a vital Test for England and there was no way I would risk breaking down and leaving the side a bowler short. . . .

England eventually won that particular Test in fine style
– by an innings and 14 runs.

from

Christmas and the New Year: A Masque for the Fireside

EDWIN LEES

Edwin Lees was a notable Worcestershire naturalist of the last century who, with two friends, founded the Worcestershire Naturalists' Club in 1847. Earlier, he had set up in business as a master printer and bookseller, and was soon writing, printing and publishing his own works. Among these was this delightful Christmas 'play' of 1828 which would have proved extremely popular at a time when fireside entertainment was largely home-produced. Lees's introduction to it — from which the following extracts are taken — is an informative commentary on his thoughts about the festive season. The masque itself, of which just the opening chorus is reproduced here, is a charmingly constructed composition, in which the main characters are Old Year, Christmas and New Year, aided by various choruses of children.

However the philosopher may smile at the arbitrary observance of particular times and seasons, there is something in the composition of the human mind that clings with tenacity and interest to such celebrations, and to the solemnities of new eras of time. There is a charm impressed upon the imagination, in the fancied passing out of one era of time into another – we are arrived at the conclusion of all that might have charmed us, and we are conscious that the history recorded in the pages of the dying era, is fixed in characters that cannot be obliterated; and we cast our eyes anxiously forward amidst the gloom and uncertainty of a coming period, that may bring us unexpected happiness, or unfold prospects of cheerless misery.

The opening of a New Year has been eagerly fixed upon by most civilised nations, from very early ages, as a starting point from which to commence the race of life afresh; to receive gifts and condolements, as it were, for past losses; and to prune the wings of hope for a fresh flight through the clouds and sunshine of the rolling year.

The Persians observe their *Noorooz*, or New Year's Day, on 21st March, which is a day of high solemnity with them. Their ancient monarchs were saluted on this occasion by a young man, habited in a fanciful dress, who personated the New Year, and who entered the king's bedchamber the moment the sun appeared above the horizon. On being asked who he was, he replied: 'I am the first day of the first week, of the first month of the New Year'. The great officers of state then entered with various presents, after which followed the different ranks of subjects.

The Chinese observe their New Year on 15th February, on which occasion they proceed to their temples before sunrise, 'while it is yet dark', dressed in their gayest apparel, with candles and incense, and make offerings before the altars of their idols.

The Romans were in the habit of observing the New Year

The symbolic entry of the New Year, an illustration from
the seasonal masque written and printed by Edwin Lees

by making presents, and paying and receiving congratulatory
visits. Roman inscriptions are still extant, 'wishing a happy
New Year to you'.

The ancient Druids of Gaul and Britain were accustomed,
on certain days, to cut the sacred mistletoe with a golden
knife, in a forest dedicated to the gods, and to distribute its
branches with much ceremony, as New Year's gifts, among
the people. The mistletoe has perhaps been uninterruptedly
used, as an embellishment to the season, from the Druidical to
the present times.

In our own times the festivities of Christmas seem to absorb
the observances of the New Year, in a great measure; and the

general cry among the populace is 'A merry Christmas and a
happy New Year when it comes'. The usual hospitalities of
Christmas are not forgotten, and the ancient yule block is still
lighted up on Christmas Eve in many farmhouses.

*The masque opens with this song by a 'chorus of boys', and
the setting is 'a long avenue of leafless lime trees, with an
antique mansion at its extremity'.*

Welcome Christmas, welcome mirth!
Welcome to the blazing hearth!
Welcome to the joys of home!
Long expected Christmas – come!

Care not for the driving snow,
Care not for the frost below;
Come beneath the shelt'ring dome;
Long expected Christmas – come!

Speed along the slipp'ry slide,
With the quiv'ring snowflake glide;
From your long excursive roam,
Welcome to our happy home!

Welcome Christmas, welcome mirth!
Welcome to the blazing hearth!
Welcome to the joys of home!
Long expected Christmas – come!

from

A Wyre Forest Diary

SIMON FLETCHER

The Wyre Forest near Bewdley is one of relatively few tracts of ancient woodland still surviving in England. In 1981, Simon Fletcher's deep appreciation of the forest's history and its wildlife, led him to write this expressive diary recording the life of the forest month by month. These are some of his thoughts for December.

The final month of the year with the shortest days and sometimes the coldest, December is a time for staying indoors and looking out at the natural world. The year has come full circle: we are back where we started. The forest is not a welcoming place in the winter.

A bird table with a few scraps of bread and some nuts will bring the wild birds to your window and you can watch the brave antics of the robin as he struts in the snow.

This is a time for log fires and hospitality when the holly, ivy and the mistletoe are brought inside to brighten the humblest cottage. Outside the land lies bleak with only a few colourful leaves still hanging on the winter boughs.

The holly and mistletoe, surrounded by tradition and
superstition

It is traditional to bring holly and mistletoe into the home
at Christmas, but few people are aware of the origin of this
custom although it has been practised since time immemorial.

It seems likely that in the beginning these plants were
brought into halls and hovels out of a superstitious belief that
they would protect the residents. Holly, in its greenery, was
specially suitable for protection in the dead of the year,
although it was effective at all times and in many ways. No
doubt a function of the holly in the home was to deal, not only
with demons and witches, but with house goblins – its berries
being red were powerful against evil.

Working the holly into Christian beliefs was not difficult, as
its parts relate closely to specific areas of the Christian
mythology. The following symbolism is found in the carol
'The Holly and the Ivy', representing the birth and the passion
of Christ. It was thorny and the berries were red – the crown of
thorns and the drops of blood combined. The blossom is white
as milk or the lily flower, symbolising the innocence and the
fecundity of the virgin birth.

But even without religious associations, holly would naturally have been used to brighten people's homes in the leafless
and flowerless depths of December. And in the Wyre Forest
where the holly is an exceptionally common shrub, it is often
harvested at Christmastime and made up into wreaths and
crosses to commemorate, or rather embellish, the graves of the
dead.

It is often forgotten that the holly also has a trunk and that
its wood was, at one time, used by townspeople and
countryfolk alike.

Apart from the wood, the bark has always been held in high
esteem by countrymen, since they made from it a sticky
substance called birdlime. The slimy bark, which is grey and
smooth, was beaten up into a pulp and then smeared on the
branches of trees, and in this way small birds would become
stuck. It should be added that the use of birdlime has died out,
thankfully.

The mistletoe is, in anyone's estimation, an unusual plant,
being parasitic on a number of deciduous trees and yet not
hurting them. The plant has always been considered an
aphrodisiac and promoter of fertility, hence the custom of
kissing under the mistletoe. It has been brought into the home
with holly for a very long time and, like the holly, was popular
before Christianity reached these shores. The Druids, apparently, believed that an oak tree which had mistletoe growing
on it was specially chosen by the gods and would promote
fertility in their cattle. The silly Druidic mania of the
eighteenth century promoted interest in the mistletoe simply
because it was their favourite plant. So we find mistletoe being
exported from Herefordshire and Worcestershire and the
neighbouring counties by the cartload in the days of George
Jordan of Bewdley, the Victorian botanist:

Immense is the quantity that is carried through Bewdley

69

annually. I wonder where it all comes from and where it goes to. It all finds a ready sale in the populous towns in the manufacturing districts, particularly at the inns.

In Worcestershire the mistletoe bough was hung on Christmas Day in the centre of the room, and left until the following Christmas as a protection against witches and goblins. As a plant of the Christmas cycle it was a companion to the evergreen holly and ivy: its berries white; their berries red and black.

Turkeys, Grouse and the Song of the Quail

CHARLES LINES

The Victorians, with characteristic enthusiasm, liked to celebrate Christmas in the grand manner and in a variety of ways. When Charles Lines delved into the archives in 1986, he discovered these accounts of two contrasting Worcestershire occasions.

It is always fascinating – and sometimes not a little amusing – to turn the pages of old newspapers and magazines and

discover how our Victorian forbears made merry in the festive season. Those were the days when a village concert might well have proved the highlight of the year; and when staid matrons would have pored delightedly – and young ladies enviously – over accounts of gowns and jewels gracing some splendid country-house ball.

During the Christmas season in 1859, a quite magnificent banquet was given in the Guildhall at Worcester in honour of Sir John Pakington MP, and to mark the presentation of a costly shield in recognition of his twenty-four years' service as chairman of the County Quarter Sessions and his brilliant political career.

A party of 230 doubtless did full justice to a menu beginning with turtle soup and iced punch, followed by a choice of turbot with lobster sauce, crimped cod with oyster sauce, and other fish. The 'Entries', as they are rather oddly termed by *Berrow's Worcester Journal*, included 'Filet de Perdreaux au Truffes', 'Kromeskys à la Russe' (whatever they were), oyster vol-au-vents, and pork cutlets with 'tomata'. (Tomatoes were then a rarity, and this spelling was sometimes used.)

But these were mere preliminaries, for the main course comprised 'Baron of Beef', haunches and patties of venison, saddles of mutton, turkeys, boiled or roast, hams, pigeon pies, boiled fowls, roast chickens, and tongue, as well as pheasant, hare and grouse.

Then there were jellies, meringues, Neapolitan gâteaux, fruit tarts, 'Blakeney Pudding', plum pudding, iced pudding and mince pies. 'Sardines' as a solitary savoury sounds rather an anti-climax, but the gallant diners – stomachs permitting – could hardly have complained at the dessert which followed.

Raised seats were provided for the ladies ('some of the élite of the county') who, poor souls, apparently got nothing to eat, and only 'entered the room at the termination of the repast',

Worcester's Guildhall at Christmastime. One memorable
seasonal banquet was held here in 1859

though they 'evinced much interest in the post-prandial
proceedings', which included some long speeches. By that
time, one imagines, most of the menfolk must have been
happily dozing.

In 1882, a seasonal concert was held in the National School
at Hanbury near Droitwich, when a large gathering was
entertained by the local gentry and their friends. Lady
Georgina Vernon, two of her sons and the Reverend F.W.
Piercy, sang a glee called 'Hark the Vesper Hymn is Stealing',
followed by the 'stirring and always favourite' 'The Hardy
Norseman's House of Yore'. Next came 'The Wreck of the
Hesperus', 'delivered with much feeling' by the Honourable
and Reverend Arthur B. Hamilton, who obliged with an
encore (shades of 'The Death of Nelson') called 'The Officer's
Funeral'.

72

The lengthy programme also included Haydn's 'Toy Symphony', 'which excited great interest from its novel features'. It was 'excellently rendered', with Miss Hamilton playing the trumpet, Miss Ogilvy imitating a nightingale, and her sister (they were the rector's daughters) impersonating both the cuckoo and quail. The Hanbury Parish Club, one is pleased to note, was 'the gainer to the amount of £5. 17s. 6d'.

It was all a far cry from the festivities at Worcester, but in the days when even the wireless or the cinema were undreamed of, it must have given genuine pleasure.

Father Christmas

ANONYMOUS – A ONE-TIME INMATE OF LONG LARTIN PRISON

In 1983, the Governor of Long Lartin Prison at South Littleton near Evesham, published a collection of poems by inmates of the prison, under the title Images From Within. *Apart from giving expression to the inmates' latent literary talents, the book also provided a means of raising funds for the Summerfield School for Children with Impaired Hearing at Malvern. The inmate who wrote this Christmas poem was obviously reflecting on his own childhood as he put pen to paper within the prison walls.*

73

· A Worcestershire Christmas ·

My Dad thinks that I don't know,
But I found out long ago.
Every year it's the same old game,
He creeps about under another name.
Each year I try to stay awake,
And many traps I devise and make:
One year I tied a string to my toe
To trip him up on the way he would go.
But he was more clever than I thought,
And that Christmas was not caught.
This year I've got one for him –
Two pounds of flour in a tin!
On the door it balances steady
To tip and spill when it is ready.
I fall asleep as I always do
But wake with a start round about two;
There are clouds of white all about,
And footprints leading out.
My bag of toys lies by the door

And there's scatter all across the floor.
I follow the footprints to Mum and Dad's room,
I listen to my Dad's voice boom –
'Wake up, Mother, and look and see
What the little devil has done to me!'
My Mum woke up and said, 'Oh dear!
What he's done is quite clear.'
I would like to have seen my Dad standing there
With all that flour in his hair,
But I crept away and went to bed.
The next day, nothing was said
But I knew I'd broken all the laws
And proved my Dad was Santa Claus!
What I've told you is quite true,
I think I must explain to you.
You see, my father is that very man
Who on Christmas Eve visits all he can.
I hope you always get what you desire,
For one day he must retire,
Then *I* must take over his wonderful work.
I just hope that *my* son in the shadows won't lurk!

A Nightingale at Christmas

JOHN LESLIE

The celebrated Victorian soprano Jenny Lind – known universally as 'the Swedish Nightingale' – made her home at Wynd's Point in Malvern. She delighted audiences as much in Worcestershire and the Midlands generally, as she did on the international stage, and in this account by John Leslie he recaptures the excitement of the great singer's Christmas charity performance in Birmingham in 1848.

Voluntarily caged in Birmingham Town Hall, Jenny Lind's appearance in the Christmas week of 1848 was notable not only for its charitable gesture on behalf of the new Queen's Hospital, but also for the significant stage that the Swedish Nightingale's career had reached.

She was only twenty-eight, but a decade of continental triumphs in *Roberto*, *Sonnambula*, *Norma* and *The Huguenots* followed her like a glittering train. Meyerbeer had composed an opera and other works especially for her, and she had won the intimate friendship of Mendelssohn who had persuaded her to come to England, where she had set the capital afever. Despite all this, she had always felt that a theatrical career was not the highest possible for her, and during her English tour decided to renounce the theatre for good, in favour of the

Jenny Lind, Malvern's 'Swedish Nightingale', whose
outstanding soprano voice delighted her Victorian audiences

concert platform. Her last appearance in an opera was in May
1849, so that her charity performance in aid of the Queen's
Hospital was in the nature of a bridgehead, linking her two
careers.

The new Birmingham hospital was estimated to cost
£8,746, and already £2,000 had been contributed between the
Chancellor of the Diocese of Lichfield and the Reverend D.L.
Warneford, while an Artisan's Penny Fund had realised a
further £935 1*s*. 3*d*. Building began, but the estimate had still
to be met, and an appeal was made by the Hospital Committee
to Jenny Lind in Malvern, who promptly and graciously
agreed to a charity performance.

The doors were opened, that Thursday evening, at 6 p.m.,

77

· *A Worcestershire Christmas* ·

Wynd's Point, Malvern, Jenny Lind's former home

the concert to begin at 7 p.m., and in spite of the *Gazette*'s smug assertion that the assembly was drawn there solely by charitable motive and not, as in previous concerts, to fill the grasping hand of some London theatre manager, it was very much a social occasion. An orchids-and-ermine affair; it *had* to be at a guinea and half-a-guinea a seat in 1848.

The artistes in support of Jenny Lind were Madame Lozana, Signors Belletti and Labache, and Mr Charles Hallé, pianist, with the Band of the 5th Dragoons in attendance. The programme was presented in two parts, and devoted largely to Rossini who was then very much in vogue.

The overture to *Semiramide* by the 5th Dragoons, was a natural introduction to Jenny Lind's first song, the duet from the same opera, in which she was accompanied by Signor

78

Labache. Her entrance, which seemed to afford herself and the gathering equal pleasure, was the signal for a tidal wave of applause. Glowing with delight, she smiled upon the crowded floor and the glittering horseshoe of the balcony, where half the output of the Birmingham jewellery trade appeared to be on display.

The applause receded, the duet began and the brilliant soprano voice of Jenny Lind, first alternating then merging with that of the valiant Labache, astonished the audience with its volume. Yet her gentlest note, her tenderest whisper, could seek out every ear, such was its purity and range.

When the duet was over, Jenny Lind remained on the platform for her first solo, 'Di Piacer' from Rossini's *La Gazza Ladra*, and through its sparkling passages her voice roved joyfully. Enslaving her hearers completely, she would not release them until the last bell-like note had died away. The applause was tremendous. The audience called for an encore.

A Fantasia for Flute by Remusat, preceded Jenny Lind's next appearance, a duet with Signor Belletti, from Rossini's *Il Turco*. Signor Labache rendered 'Largo de Factotum' from *Barbiére di Seviglia*, Madame Lozana an aria from *Tancredi*, and the first part of the concert closed with Jenny Lind's second solo, the 'Trio for Voice and Two Flutes' by Meyerbeer.

This was one of his works especially composed for Jenny Lind, to give full scope to her combination of facility and execution. Between voice and instruments, effect followed effect in boundless succession, and the audience was frequently perplexed as to which was which, the most elaborate runs on the flutes being so closely imitated by Mlle Lind, that it was like listening to three flutes.

The second part of the programme opened with the overture to *William Tell*, and a recital of Spanish songs by Madame Lozana. Jenny Lind's next solo, the Cavatina from *Der Freischutz*, was intended as the gem of the evening.

Unfortunately, she sang the English version, which was so colourless that her natural dramatic expression was not given full reign, and to the more discerning of the audience, if not to the singer herself, it was the one flaw in her repertoire.

She concluded her performance by joining the audience in 'God Save the Queen', when she sang the first and third verses solo. This was the first time Jenny Lind had rendered an English song in English to a Midland audience, and although it was naturally tinged with a foreign accent, her sincerity and enthusiasm were easily translatable. The phrase 'Her choicest gifts in store, on thee be pleased to pour', she sang with a special significance, as if by way of conveying her thanks for the overwhelming appreciation that her English audiences had shown her.

The concert was over but before the audience left, a presentation was made to Jenny Lind, on behalf of the grateful hospital. A rosewood cabinet, lined with velvet, contained a casket 16 inches high by 11 inches wide, inlaid with silver. Its Watteau compartments, filled in with gold and pearl, included a jewel draw, writing desk and workbox with silver scissors and cotton reels carved in pearl. Originally, the presentation was to be made on the morning before the concert, but Jenny Lind had requested that instead, it should be made immediately after her performance.

'May health, happiness and success ever attend you in your onward course of usefulness', said the Reverend Warneford, presenting the casket to the rather-more-than-useful singer. She replied that she would not forget the anxiety manifested by the committee to show her every respect. 'I am so grateful at coming among you,' Jenny Lind concluded, 'that it will not be the last time.'

The Mayor of Birmingham had invited her and the Hospital Committee to a *déjeuner* the next morning, which she attended, and afterwards delighted the manufacturers of the

casket, Messrs Jennens and Battridge of Constitution Hill, by paying them a visit. On Saturday the 31st, Jenny Lind and her retinue left for Manchester, and all the bells that rang the New Year in that night, could not match the magic of her brilliant soprano voice.

Naturally, the critics were fulsome about her, but her fellow artistes, suffering by comparison, were damned with the indulgent praise usually reserved for amateurs. Madame Lozana, making her Birmingham début, 'sang with a taste and finish that showed most marked study'. Signor Labache's duet with the Swedish Nightingale 'was tastefully sung', whilst the Band of the 5th Dragoons rendered their overtures 'with great precision and care'.

Barely honoured, faintly sung, their departure from the town was not recorded, much less were they entertained to *déjeuner* by the Mayor. But at least they could say, 'That Christmas, when I appeared with Jenny Lind . . .'

My Dear Ann: Letters From Pear Tree Cottage

ANN O'DAY MAPLES

*Shortly after the Second World War, Ann Maples and
her husband travelled from their Californian home to
holiday in Norway. While they were there, they met and
befriended a young English couple, Philip and June
Wightman, who lived at Pear Tree Cottage in the
Worcestershire village of Shelsley Beauchamp. As a result,
June struck up a regular correspondence with Ann, who, a
few years before she died in her 107th year, published a
selection of June's letters in book form. These not only evoke
a unique picture of rural Worcestershire before the influence
of urbanization, but are a charming reminder of the true
art of letter-writing. In the Christmas letter reproduced
here, June gives Ann a glimpse of life at Shelsley
Beauchamp during one festive season.*

· *A Worcestershire Christmas* ·

My dear Ann,

And in no time at all it is Christmas again, so we send you our love and wishes for a happy time and a good new year to follow.

My neighbour, Mrs Fuller and her husband Tom departed yesterday for a 'wintering' at Tintern with their son. They looked as if they were setting out on some expedition – all loaded up like beasts of burden, including cat in basket. I went down to see her on Friday, when the packing operation was almost complete, or seemed to be. Mrs Fuller said she didn't think she would be finished in time. She was in a right pickle and looked as though she were moving house instead of herself. The carpets were rolled up and tied securely, and somehow she had managed to lift them on to sofas and chairs because 'the floors get all sticky and damp, ducks, and don't do the carpets no good if they'm left lying down'.

She had done two weeks' accumulation of laundry several days before, and because of the weather (high winds and driving rain had followed the snow), she couldn't get it dry outside. So she had stoked up a wood fire in the inglenook in the living room, and another in the small sitting room, and hung the sundries round in relays. 'Things got all scorched, ducks,' she said, and she held up two pairs of drawers with brown seats.

It was the first time I had ever heard her grumble, apart from her acid comments about the opposite sex – 'Men ent much use on the whole'. She complained of feeling cold, the house was too damp by half, and two of the oil lamps weren't working properly and only gave light on one-half of the wick.

'Makes it so difficult to do housework, ducks,' she explained. ''Cause I does all me housework at night.' So I asked her why she did the house-cleaning at night as it seemed a silly thing to do. 'Well, ducks,' she said, 'I keeps losing things and it takes me all day finding them. First I loses me brush, and

when I finds it I can't put me hands on the dustpan. Then me dusters have gone missing, and by the time I've collected everything together to make a start, it's dark.'

She asked me if I would do something for her, and I boldly agreed. 'Just come upstairs with me, ducks,' she said. So I followed her up the steep, twisting stairs, both of us climbing on all fours because there was no hand rail to steady one's ascent. All the beds were stripped, and the mattresses up-ended. Neat piles of blankets, sheets, table cloths, and everything else imaginable were stacked ready for their solitary vigil until her return in the spring. She took me through the 'hole-in-the-wall' – a half-size doorway tucked under a large oak beam – and into a wee bedroom with the roof sloping down to the floor on either side. What a sight confronted me! All along the wall of the gable end, with a minute latticed window letting in a minimum of light, there were receptacles of every description, ranging from meat baking-tins to chamber pots. The high winds of a few days before had driven the heavy rain through the perished brickwork cramped between the oak beams let in the wall. There were enormous dust-sheets and large polythene bags on the floor, and what with the furniture and the 'rain-catchers' there was hardly room to move.

'Will you have the front door key, ducks?' Mrs Fuller asked when we were safely downstairs again. 'Not to put yourself out though, ducks. But if we gets some more heavy rain, can you just pop in and empty the water out of all them things and give the old sheets a bit of a squeeze-out, 'cause the rain don't just trickle in, it pours in.'

I assured her I would see to everything. So if we have a very wet Christmas, spare a thought for me giving the dust-sheets a 'squeeze-out' and emptying chamber pots flowing over with rain water.

And on that wet note, my love to everyone, and, as always,

Fondest love to you,

June

Christmas with Harry Bailey

FRED ARCHER

Fred Archer's third contribution recalls two of the highlights of the festive season at Ashton-under-Hill – the Boxing Day party at the home of his father's business partner, Harry Bailey, and the Sunday School Christmas tea.

Most Christmases in Ashton-under-Hill, we visited Dad's partner, Harry Bailey, on Boxing Day. We drove to his house in Dad's 1913 Sunbeam tourer at six o'clock for a high tea. It seems odd now how the food at the parties of our youth was anticipated with such pleasure, and still holds strong memories: the cold ham off the bone, the crisp celery – Harry Bailey grew a pink variety in his kitchen garden – masses of mince pies, with real mincemeat made from Bittersweet apples from a local orchard, strong sweet tea, and castle-shaped chocolate blancmange with a moulded lion on top. Then, equally memorable, were the shadows from the Aladdin oil lamp on the window blinds, and the crackling sound of burning logs.

After we had pulled the crackers, Harry Bailey came into the dining room with a peck basket of walnuts from trees in the rickyard. He produced a brass counter like a spinning top from a drawer and said to Dad, 'Your first spin, Tom.'

Meanwhile all the party had been served with about twenty walnuts each; the walnuts in the middle were spare. As the counter came to rest on the table, with one of its legends uppermost, perhaps reading 'Put Two', Dad put two of the nuts to join the heap in the middle. The game of Put and Take was under way. Sometimes the brass counter read 'Take All', and the lucky player took all the nuts from the centre of the table. You may well say, 'What a feeble game.' But it wasn't – not before radio and television had taken over our Christmas celebrations.

Another game we played at that party was called Pit. The cards were dealt and we strove to collect enough of one variety

Mrs Harry Bailey of Ashton-under-Hill feeding the Christmas poultry. She was the wife of Fred Archer's father's business partner

to claim a corner, as we exchanged the cards marked wheat, oats, barley, beans and rye across the table. When a set of one variety of cereals was in hand we shouted, 'Corner on barley' or 'Corner on rye', as the case was. What a game! What a party!

After singing a few carols around the piano and listening to the local bell-ringers singing their selection on the lawn outside, we went home, pockets bulging with walnuts and apples. But we usually met Harry Bailey again a few days later at the Chapel Sunday School Christmas tea and social.

Here in the recreation room under the corrugated iron roof of this First World War army hut, it all happened. The joint efforts of Harry Bailey and William Boulton made this party go with a swing. I reckon the adults enjoyed it as much as the children, for they often played what always seemed fairly rough sports. Musical chairs, as I remember, was more like a rugby scrum as the farm lads shoved and pushed and sprawled on the dusty floorboards.

As William Boulton's voice began to get husky towards nine o'clock and we settled down to a quieter game of Winking, Harry Bailey came through the door with a waggon rope. We sat with him by the stove waiting while the young men and girls from the farm houses ran around the circle of chairs and played Clap and Run. Then William Boulton took a bunch of keys from his pocket and organised 'A-Hunting We Will Go'.

The atmosphere by then was pretty warm. Men's jackets were hung on the coat hooks or laid across the billiard table. Then came the *pièce de résistance* as Harry Bailey uncoiled his rope which stretched the length of the recreation room. Two sturdy men of the land picked their teams and here in this old army hut, a genuine tug-of-war took place.

As heavy boots slid along the floorboards and one team and then another held sway, we cheered our group on. At one point the rope broke, catapulting one team on to the stage and the other against the door.

By now the younger children had gone home clutching their presents. Some had scored fifty-two marks for full Sunday School attendance during the year, a feat announced by Father Christmas, alias William Boulton. They took with them, besides their presents from the Christmas tree, oranges, apples and more of Harry Bailey's walnuts. Then the waggon rope would be hung in the barn until haymaking time next July.

So that was how Christmas under Bredon Hill was celebrated by a group of Chapel folk. I wonder who first thought of having a tug-of-war in the recreation room? It was certainly a highlight of that do-it-yourself Christmas party, long before we became glued to the televison screen and just stared our Christmases away.

Elgar and Christmas – 2

This second reminder of an Elgarian Christmas takes us back to 1929. Elgar was living at Marl Bank on Rainbow Hill in Worcester, and on his Christmas card that year, he did not include a verse of his own composition, but borrowed one from the American poet Walt Whitman.

With Sir Edward Elgar's Good Wishes
for Christmas and the New Year.

88

· A Worcestershire Christmas ·

Elgar country – Malvern Priory in the snow, a scene which
the composer would still instantly recognize

I think I could turn and live with animals, they are so placid
   and self-contain'd;
They do not sweat and whine about their condition;
They do not lie awake in the dark and weep for their sins;
They do not make me sick discussing their duty to God;
Not one is dissatisfied – not one is demented with the mania
   of owning things;
Not one kneels to another, nor to his kind that lived thousands
   of years ago;
Not one is respectable or industrious over the whole earth.

Walt Whitman

Marl Bank,
Rainbow Hill,
Worcester.   24th December, 1929.

· *A Worcestershire Christmas* ·

Among those who received the Christmas card was fellow composer Frank Bridge who, a few days later, sent Elgar this acknowledgement from his home in London.

My Dear Sir Edward,

Your card has only just reached me and I feel I must thank you for it. The quotation is so well-chosen that I envy you your thought of it.

But, how many animals could live with us?

With all good wishes for the New Year.

Yours very sincerely,
Frank Bridge

from

The Christmas Box

FRANCIS BRETT YOUNG

Francis Brett Young was born in 1884 at Halesowen and for much of his life he lived at Craycombe, the elegant Adam house still standing at Fladbury, where he wrote many of his novels and other works. He died in 1954, and his ashes are interred in Worcester Cathedral. Among his lesser-known books is The Christmas Box *which he*

· *A Worcestershire Christmas* ·

Francis Brett Young, whose ashes are interred in Worcester Cathedral

originally wrote for The Strand Magazine *in 1936. It is a delightful story, abridged here, which recounts the Christmas experiences of a Worcestershire labourer, who after army service in the First World War, set up a greengrocer's shop in the Lambeth district of London.*

The moment he opened his eyes on the morning of Christmas Eve – and even before that – Jim Higgins knew for certain that the weather had changed. Last night's wireless forecast, bellowed at him from the loud-speaker next door, had already assured him that it would.

But Jim Higgins needed no wireless to warn him that the wind was backing to the east. He possessed a meteorological instrument of his own, infallibly sensitive: the stump of the right leg which Private J. Higgins, 36049, Worcestershire

Regiment, had mislaid at Gheluvelt. The first westward waft was sufficient to arouse in that matted nexus of fibrous tissue and nerve-endings premonitory twinges. When the east wind blew in earnest it stabbed his stump with needles ice-cold or white-hot. And no other wind did that.

For all he knew he might only have slept a few hours. He guessed it was early – how early he dreaded to know – until, suddenly, the boom of Big Ben, drifting over the river, beat in on his grateful ears the announcement that day – if not light – had come at last.

Six o'clock. That wasn't too bad. Emily, his wife, lying beside him, still slept, gently grinding her teeth. He could hear their fifteen-year-old daughter and only child, Nellie, snoring peacefully in the tiny room next door: she was a terror for snoring, their Nellie, just like a grown man.

He thought tenderly of Nellie lying there fast asleep, with her mouth wide open; he thought tenderly of Emily beside him, grinding her teeth; for he was a 'family man', and these two, in their different ways, were the only possessions in which he took pride, which he was prepared to defend at any cost.

The fact that both slept so soundly and could count on at least another hour of blessed oblivion constrained him to lie motionless; but though he was itching to move, he knew that moving would make no difference to the ache in his leg. Since sleep, for himself, was out of the question, he supposed he might just as well try to lie still and think, until the strokes of another hour from the great clock over the river gave him a valid excuse for rousing them.

Yet a man couldn't doze with an icy-hot needle jagging at him, and pain coloured his thoughts.

As Jim lay there, he thought of money – he always did – and of how little he possessed, despite the new air of hope

92

which pervaded the country after the war ended. He thought, too, of the battles in which he won the Military Medal and Mons Star; of the trauma of losing his leg and of the eventual fitting of its artificial replacement. He remembered his decision not to return to Worcestershire as a labourer on the land, and how he had saved money from his pension to start his greengrocery business and settle down in Lambeth with Emily. Now, he pondered, life was very tough. His customers — many unemployed and on the dole — owed him money, and if he pressed them for payment he would lose them. His mind went back to his pre-war years at Monk's Norton in Worcestershire, where he tended his garden, sowing and harvesting in season, and winning prizes at the Chaddesbourne spring flower show.

Such themes were unseasonable, he thought, in any case. This was Christmas Eve: there would be three (probably four) long months with grim alternations of fog and slush and sleet and snow before one had any right to go dreaming of spring. Yet even the winter, he told himself, had seemed somehow shorter and less bitter at Monk's Norton than here in Lambeth. The season he feared and hated now, had been rich in those far-off days, with peculiar delights. As a boy, he could remember counting the weeks, then the days, to Christmas; and Christmas Day itself had been more than worth the excited anticipation.

Lying there, Jim Higgins remembered wistfully the Christmas days of his childhood in Worcestershire. Like everything else that had happened before the war, their incidents were more highly coloured than anything that had happened after it. He could remember walking to church under the bare black branches of the great Monk's Norton elms over a frost-bound road: the thin white ice bridging the frozen ruts crinkled

Hoar frost adds a picturesque quality to the banks of the
Avon at Pershore, a scene close to Francis Brett Young's
former home at Craycombe

under his feet, and the pale sky above the elm-twigs tufted
with last year's rook-nests was so high and cloudless that the
voices of the bells that issued from their icicled louvres went
singing through it unimpeded, exulting in an unusual freedom and laughing over the land.

   Inside the church the air was stonily cold, yet not so cold as
it seemed on ordinary Sundays in winter; for the congregation
was double its usual size and these human radiators warmed
the air about them. The whole church wore a cheerful air in its
festal array of bright-berried holly. When the people sang
'While Shepherds' and 'Christians Awake', you felt this was
more like a jolly family party than a religious service. As they

94

came out of the porch they lingered amid the gravestones wishing each other a Merry Christmas and a Happy New Year; but he, the boy, with his church-sharpened appetite, was only thinking of the Christmas dinner his mother had stayed at home to cook: a succulent goose with apple sauce and sage-and-onion; a plum pudding, with always the chance of one's teeth triumphantly gritting on a threepenny-bit, and, after that, one of the oranges (an exotic fruit, unknown at other seasons) which Miss Abberley or Mrs Sheldon-Smith had sent down – with a pound packet of tea, perhaps – from the Manor or the Grange.

Christmas, of course, was above all else a festival for children, and the things he remembered were those that gave pleasure and excitement to a child; yet, thinking it over, Jim Higgins couldn't believe that, even for children, a London Christmas could have quite the same magic as this. He felt sorry that Nellie had never experienced, would never experience, the joys he remembered. . . .

Once more Big Ben boomed. Eight o'clock. Jim Higgins blinked and rubbed his eyes. He must have been dozing after all. He turned over, daring at last, to stretch his legs. Emily, too, turned over and yawned. She stared at him with unseeing eyes.

'What time was that, Jim?'

'Eight o'clock.'

'Well, I never!' She shivered. 'Nippy, isn't it?'

'Well it ought to be, didn't it? Christmas Eve and all. That's what they call seasonable.'

'It's foggy, too. I can smell it.' She sniffed.

Jim rolled out of bed. He strapped on his leg, dressed hurriedly to escape from the cold, and clumped downstairs.

Jim made a cup of tea for himself and Emily, opened the shop door, and swept the pavement. He pushed his empty

95

hand-cart outside, ready for his daily limping trek to Covent Garden to buy produce, and carefully displayed the remnants of yesterday's stock on the stand in front of the shop. Emily and Nellie came down to breakfast.

There was some quality, indeed, in this pale golden morning (despite the east wind): this, together with a half-realized consciousness that it was Christmas Eve and that tomorrow would be Christmas Day – a feeling of release and gaiety already mysteriously communicated to the very air by the desires and hopes and aspirations of no fewer than seven millions of Londoners, who, awake at that moment, had become aware of the same thrilling circumstance.

Even the rashers of bacon with which he symmetrically decorated the frying-pan sizzled merrily and released an ambrosial, mouth-watering aroma. For the first time since he had opened his eyes on the fog that day, Jim Higgins felt that it was a romantic and exciting thing to be alive and hungry and cutting thick slices of stale bread at half-past-eight on a winter morning.

Jim pushed back his chair and picked his teeth meditatively.

'About time I was moving along, I reckon. Give your dad a kiss, Nellie,' he said, pulling her pig-tailed head backward, hugging her to him and implanting a hungry smack on either cheek.

Nellie wriggled. 'Oh, Dad, what a beard you've got!' she cried. 'You're all over horrid bristles.'

'You wait till you see me shaved for Christmas,' Jim laughed.

'About time too, I should say,' Mrs Higgins put in scornfully; then, moved by an obvious association of ideas: 'Mind, don't forget that mistletoe! I promised Mrs Parker a bunch.'

'It'd take more than a bunch to make any man in his senses kiss Mrs Parker.'

'Don't be soft, Jim. What's that got to do with it? Kisses indeed!' Mrs Higgins was not receptive of jokes at that time of the morning. 'She don't need a lot. Just a sprig, like, to 'ang on the chandelier. And don't buy more than that. We can't afford to be landed with more than we can sell; and mistletoe's off from tomorrow, don't forget that! Leave me plenty of change in the till, dear.'

Change in the till, dear! That was a subject much better avoided. As it was he could barely scrape together enough to cover this morning's purchases. This last week, for some reason or another, had been the slackest in the whole year. People were doing their Christmas shopping, he supposed; and when they shopped for Christmas they forsook their usual tradesmen to whom they owed money and went streaming away in droves to the more prosperous thoroughfares, buzzing in and out of the doors of the multiple grocery shops like bees on the step of a hive, flattening their noses against the breath-misted windows of Woolworth's and Marks and Spencer's to see what new bargains were pranked out in cotton-wool snow and tinsel and frost of mica, standing to gape at the pale cascades of fat geese and turkeys encrusted with holly hung in front of the poulterers' windows, or, more often still, merely clogging the pavements in aimless promenade.

He took from the till as much as he dared, slipped out of the shop, and lifted the shafts of his hand-cart.

Jim pushed his hand-cart through the streets on this busy Christmas Eve morning, a weary journey he did each day. Delicious aromas from warmly-lit coffee shops assailed him as he passed, and he was aware of a nagging hunger despite his rashers at breakfast-time. But he resisted the temptation to go inside, and plodded on to the market where he was cheerily greeted by the many traders who knew him. One of these, Mr Levi, gave him some Christmas oranges for his wife, and he then set about buying the day's stock for his shop. Next came the search for some mistletoe.

Jim Higgins crossed the street hurriedly. On the other side stood a farm-lorry stacked with fourteen-pound bunches of mistletoe, and holly with berries the colour of sealing wax. A red-faced countryman in clay-mired corduroys was unloading it. Jim approached and read the name painted on the side of it below the driver's seat:

> George Collins
> Goodrest Farm
> Monk's Norton, Worcs.

The sight of these words brought a sudden glow to his spirits and an overwhelming wistfulness, for the village from which the lorry-load of mistletoe had come was that in which he had been born. The red mud on the tyres of the lorry and on its driver's corduroys was his native marl. To think of it!

Jim spoke to the driver eagerly: 'You driven up here from Monk's Norton this morning?'

'Ay, started at half-past-five, afore it was light.'

'I come from Monk's Norton myself, though I've not been in them parts for twenty-four year. There wasn't much mistletoe there from what I remember. More down E'esham way.'

'That's right. There bain't much now. This here come off a lot of old apple trees up at the Mill,'

He laughed as he went on unloading the bunches of mistletoe. Jim lent him a hand until the lorry was emptied.

'Look here . . .' Jim came to the point. 'Could you spare us a bit of mistletoe? I should like to feel I'd got summat that come from Monk's Norton in the 'ouse. I'll pay for it mind.'

The young man laughed. 'You've no call to pay for what's broken. You be welcome to all you can find.'

The floor of the lorry was littered with broken branches from the sweepings of which Jim made up an armful. All the time his mind was full of the yearning tenderness he had experienced in bed that morning when he thought of the old country Christmases. He was so engrossed in this dream that he did not hear behind him a sudden splinter and cracking of wood. Mr Levi's man, Joe, ran across the street to call him:

'Mr Higgins, Mr Higgins! A lorry's backed into your hand-cart.'

Jim limped over hurriedly, still carrying his armful of mistletoe. The terrible news was true. A big van, backing, had crashed into the hand-cart standing by the kerb. The whole of one side was stove in. All the boxes of vegetables had been overturned. Their contents were scattered on the roadway and one wheel lay loose. Jim gazed at the wreckage in despair.

Already a circle of idlers had closed on the scene and stood gazing stupidly. The sight of them infuriated Jim Higgins. Some sniggered and turned away; some others continued stupidly staring. Mr Levi waddled out and scratched his head.

'That's made a pretty mess, hasn't it? The beggar ought to have stopped. Anyone taken his number?'

Of course the beggar ought to have stopped, the onlookers agreed, and nobody had taken his number, nor did anyone move to help. Jim ruefully picked up the wheel. Then another voice spoke. It was that of the red-faced young man from Monk's Norton who had shambled across the road.

'Well, this is a fine show,' he said. 'Still, it might have been worse. I reckon we can fix this up all right: the wheel isn't broken. Anyone got a hammer and some nails? You pick up

99

your stuff Mr Higgins, while I have a go at it. I'm a bit of a wheelwright myself.'

Now everybody suddenly wanted to help. While the young man hammered away at the wheel, other hands picked up the fruit and vegetables that had rolled into the gutter. Jim scrabbled among them, wiping the mud from leeks and cabbages and cauliflowers with his red pocket-handkerchief. The attitude of the spectators was no longer callous. It was as if the young countryman's sudden intervention had crystallized an indeterminate mood. Jim found himself surrounded by a general and cheering benevolence. Even the grand Mr Levi himself condescended to stoop to the gutter and pick up oranges. Within ten minutes the detached wheel had been hammered into shape and fixed, hardly more precariously than before, to its axle. All the scattered vegetables had been crammed back into their boxes. The splintered cart-tail was nailed up and forced into line.

The young man from Monk's Norton scanned his work doubtfully:

'It bain't what you'd rightly call a carpenter's job,' he said, 'but I reckon you'll manage to get it home all right if so be as you're careful.'

'It never was a carpenter's job,' Mr Levi laughed. 'That barrow's like me and some of the rest of us: it's suffering from Anno Domini.' As he surveyed the patched hand-cart and Jim's troubled face, his conscience smote him. He slipped his hand in his pocket and pulled out a handful of silver.

'Look here, Jim,' he said. 'You and me have been doing business for a good many years, and I don't believe I've ever given you a Christmas Box for yourself.' He picked out a half-crown; then thoughtfully changed it for a florin. 'Suppose you buy yourself a packet of fags and a bottle of beer to drink my health in tomorrow.'

Jim accepted the florin and pushed his laden cart back to the shop, complete with the oranges for Emily and the mistletoe. When he arrived home he found his wife in a state of anger and his daughter tearful. It transpired that a stranger had come into the shop requesting change for a florin. Nellie found that there was only 1s. 9d. in the till, so the man accepted it, said she could keep the balance as a Christmas box, and left the shop. But the florin proved to be a dud.

Emily flung the coin contemptuously on the counter. It fell with a leaden thud. Jim picked it up and examined it.

'That's a stumer, all right, and a pretty bad one at that. But there's no call to make the child cry, Em. She knew no better. And what does it matter anyway? Here you are, Nell. This one's all right.'

He laughed; Mr Levi's florin rang on the counter like a silver sleigh-bell.

'Oh, give over. Don't be so soft,' Mrs Higgins said fiercely. 'What difference does it make? It all comes out of the till. We're two shillings short just the same.'

Then Jim Higgins blew up. It was not often that he blew up; but on this rare occasion he did so good and proper.

'Look here, I've had enough of you and your grousing,' he shouted. 'Makes no difference, don't it? I'll tell you the difference it makes. This 'ere money's got nothing whatever to do with you: it's a present a gentleman give me. It's gone into the till.' He flung it in viciously.

'Come on Nellie,' he said. 'Give us a hand with this stuff, kid. There's nothing to cry over.'

As father and daughter unloaded the hand-cart, there came the sound of an organ-grinder playing not far away. Jim was in no mood for this kind of entertainment, and he

*stumped towards the unfortunate culprit to remonstrate
with him. On discovering that the organ-grinder was also
one-legged, and that he was wearing the Mons Star, the
General Service and Victory medals, Jim questioned him.
It transpired that he was a former wartime comrade,
Tubby Bomford, who had served with Jim and who had
since hit hard times.*

'Come in, Tubby old pal. What d'you say to a cup of tea?'

'I don't mind if I do, Jim. I've had no breakfast this
morning. Ne'er a bite.'

'You haven't? We'll soon put that right.' Immediately Jim
was transported. 'Here, Em,' he called, 'put the kettle on
quick and cut us some bread and butter. There's an old pal of
mine, Mr Bomford, turned up. Come on, Tubby, walk in and
mind that there step. You can leave the piano outside. This is
our Nellie – a great girl she is — and that's my missus.'

They sat down on opposite sides of the kitchen table. Jim
did most of the talking, for Mr Bomford's contributions,
though he smiled and nodded continually, were impeded by
the slabs of bread smeared with margarine on which he
gorged himself like a hungry dog. They talked of old times
and places: of Ypres and the Menin Road and Wytschaete and
Gheluvelt.

'Do you mind that first Christmas we had out there,
nineteen-fourteen, Tubby?'

'I should say I did, Jim. That's twenty-three year ago to the
day, like. We was down by Armentières.'

'Ay, Armentières. That was a rum go if ever there was one!
Remember how Fritz started singing 'Oh Come All Ye
Faithful' in German, and how our chaps joined in? And then
one of our officers – Mr Ombersley, that was his name; come
from Chaddesbourne, he did – went out into No-man's-land
for a talk with one of their officers, and we fetched back a lot of

our chaps off the German wire. A rum Christmas that was: the rummest ever I knew.'

They talked of the years that had passed since the war was ended, of their small triumphs, their bitter struggles. It was clear that Tubby had had the worse time of the two. During the last six months he had been properly on the rocks.

'Still I manage to scrape along, Jim, you know. Old soldiers never die, as they say, and I keep up my spirits. It's going uphill when the streets is greasy that catches me.'

'Same here,' Jim agreed. 'I've a hand-cart I push every day back from Covent Garden.'

It was years since Jim Higgins had so completely enjoyed himself; and, oddly enough, this exaltation of common memory appeared to communicate itself to all their sur-roundings. As they sat in the little room at the back, Mrs Higgins forgot to sulk and stood by, smiling and listening, or darted to and fro as the little shop filled with customers. The whole street, it seemed, was unusually eager to buy Jim's wares that morning. People came in a steady stream and bought in a lavish, uncritical spirit. Money clinked in the till, and the boxes he had brought back from the market steadily emptied.

At length Mr Bomford pushed back his chair and wiped his mouth with his sleeve.

'That's the best blow-out I've had for weeks,' he said, '*and* the best bit of talk. Thank you, Jim. Thank you kindly. I reckon I ought to be getting on with my round.'

As Jim came abreast of the counter, a thought struck him. He halted and opened the till.

'What d'you want, dear?' said Emily.

'Oh, nothing, love,' he replied.

But it wasn't really nothing. Among the brown coppers and tarnished shillings and sixpences he was searching for the virgin silver of Mr Levi's new florin. Greatly daring, and

103

always conscious of his wife's watchful eye, he extracted the coin and slipped it into Tubby Bomford's hand.

''Ere you are, kid,' he whispered. 'This'll do for a Christmas Box.' He turned round to avoid being thanked, and faced a fat woman customer. 'Yes, madam?' he said with a flourish. 'And what can I do for you?'

Christmas Carol

G.A. STUDDERT KENNEDY

The Reverend G.A. Studdert Kennedy – better known, even to this day, long after his death, as Woodbine Willie – was a remarkable army chaplain in the First World War whose sheer charisma had a profoundly stirring effect on all who met him. In civilian life he was the vicar of St Paul's Church in Worcester, and he was also a notable writer of both prose and verse. This charming carol is one of the many poems he wrote reflecting the sincere Christian belief he held throughout his life.

Come worship the King,
That little white thing,
Asleep on His Mother's soft breast.
Ye bright stars bow down,
Weave for Him a crown,
Christ Jesus by angels confessed.

Come, children, and peep,
But hush ye, and creep
On tiptoe to where the Babe lies:
Then whisper His name
And lo! like a flame
The Glory light shines in His eyes.

Come, strong men, and see
This high mystery,
Tread firm where the shepherds have trod,
And watch, 'mid the hair
Of the Maiden so fair,
The five little fingers of God.

Come, old men and grey,
The star leads the way,
It halts, and your wanderings cease;
Look down on His face,
Then, filled with His grace,
Depart ye, God's servants, in peace.

Christmas at
Worcester in
Medieval Times

*This evocative account of Christmas celebrations nearly five
centuries ago, is based on the diary kept by a Prior of
Worcester. The entries were collected together in 1948 to
form the basis of an article in a local newspaper. It is
interesting to note that when the article was published, the
ancient timber roof of Worcester's Guesten Hall, to which
reference is made, was still adorning Holy Trinity Church
on Shrub Hill. It was subsequently moved to the Avoncroft
Museum of Buildings at Bromsgrove where it is now an
important attraction for visitors.*

The twelve days of Christmas – lasting from the Nativity to
the Epiphany – were great days in Worcester long ago. Before
the Reformation, when Prior John Moore ruled the monastic
house in the cloister at Worcester, there were tremendous
doings at this season in the Guesten Hall, whose sandstone
ruins remain near the Chapter House, and whose timber roof
adorns the modern church of the Holy Trinity on Shrub Hill.

Prior Moore, a jovial and hospitable old gentleman if ever
there was one, left a diary in which he recorded all manner of
events. Thanks to John Noake, the historian of a century ago,

· *A Worcestershire Christmas* ·

Worcester Cathedral, shrouded in the mists of winter. Its
now vanished Guesten Hall was once the scene of
spectacular Christmas celebrations

large portions of this strangely spelled journal, in a mixture of
ecclesiastical Latin and queer sixteenth-century English, can
be read in more understandable form today.

On Christmas Day after Evensong, and again on New Year's
Eve, the bailiff or Mayor and the Corporation 'all in skarlet
gowns', dined with the Prior in the Guesten Hall. Severn
salmon from the weirs at Hallow and Henwick (monastic
properties) formed the fish course, and there were such meats
as venison, roast swan, pigeon pasty, and coney or rabbit
cooked in dozens of ways.

The beverages were many and queerly named – mawmesey,
osey, pyment and Lippocras, for instance; they were highly
spiced and sweetened. Ale was thick and so full of sticky dregs
that the polite guest filtered it through his teeth. Wafers and

sweetmeats rounded off the meal (one likes to think of the city fathers slipping one or two into the furred sleeves of aldermanic gowns, for the children at home). There was 'a dyshe of mynce pyes' for the choirboys.

Then the tables were not merely cleared but removed altogether, and the entertainment began. Singers of 'carralls' were nothing new then, and strolling minstrels were welcome to sing for their supper. The Prior records a payment to one 'William ye Lewter for his singing and pleying in ye Christmass wicke', and no doubt William had a grand time in the monastic kitchens as well.

There were local players at Worcester, spiritual ancestors of today's dramatic societies, who were summoned to perform (and rewarded thereafter) for the Prior's guests.

The king's minstrels, 'Thomas Brandon, ye king's jogeler and servants', 'ye king's jogeler and his blynd harper' were welcomed at different times, and once they came they stayed, usually the whole twelve days.

Presents came at New Year, and from those offered to Prior John, a man of the people who came from yeoman stock at Grimley, one can get a very good idea of gifts over four hundred years ago in his walk of life.

He had a brother, Robert, a wine merchant at Bristol, from whom he bought wine for the monastery and its guests. Robert sent 'a pottel of mawmesey' as a New Year gift. The numerous tenants who farmed monastic lands, the bailiffs of manors, as well as neighbours and friends in the city and the officers of the house itself, made presents to the Prior.

The cellarer presented 'a pillow of grene and red silk for my pewe', and on another occasion a basket of oranges. These had several uses: you might eat them as a costly delicacy, or you could stick cloves in the skin and use the fruit as a perfume bottle, very serviceable in undrained streets and insanitary buildings.

Oranges came from the tenant of 'The Cardinal's Hat', still an inn under the name of the Coventry Arms. Richard of Sudbury, another neighbour, sent a pair of gloves; Lady Sandys two pieces of amber, 'the Abbot of Wynchecombe's cosyn a fyne hand napkyn', 'the bayly of Newenham eight partridges, a dysh of trowtes and greylyngs', and so on.

No wonder the Prior was able to hold such feasts for the chief citizens, when his gifts included peacocks, capons, geese, lambs, pigs, cheeses, brawns, mallards, and dozens of larks.

from

Lock Keeper's Daughter

PAT WARNER

In her childhood, Pat Warner lived by the side of the Worcester and Birmingham Canal at Tardebigge near Bromsgrove. In these recollections, she casts her mind back to a memorable Christmas in 1928.

The winter of 1928, it just snowed and snowed. We didn't see the milkman or the postman for a number of weeks. Somehow,

this seemed fairly normal in those days and we were always well prepared.

The snow would pile up along the towing path, two or three feet high – sometimes higher. And it was cold. So cold at night that it would freeze the contents of the chamber pot under the bed! I would keep warm with a hot brick wrapped in a piece of flannel. But what a pretty sight was all that snow. Clean, white snow, not dirty slushy stuff. The sun shining and long icicles hanging from the lock gates. If you looked across the reservoir from the back bedroom window, you might catch a glimpse of some wild creature which had dared venture out. You might even see a red squirrel, sitting in one of the trees, holding a hazel nut between his front paws.

I knew that if the weather didn't improve, we would be unable to visit my aunt and uncle for Christmas. They lived, I thought, on the other side of the world, but it was only Wolverhampton. All that long distance was a great adventure for me. It began with a two-mile walk to the bus stop at Tardebigge. The fare from there to Bromsgrove was 5*d.* (2 p). We would then travel to Stourbridge – another shilling (5 p) – and from there to the LMS station at Wolverhampton – one more shilling. This would take most of the day. On reaching journey's end, the Wolverhampton snow was all wet and dirty, not like the nice clean snow I was used to.

Most of Christmas Eve was passed in taking trams to visit the shops. What a good thing I liked trams and buses, because not all the dolls and sweets in England would have persuaded me to get into a car. I was terrified of motor cars. The large stores in town stayed open until 8 o'clock at night and I would be able to buy all my Christmas presents with the 2*s. 6d.* (12½p) I had saved.

We would return to my aunt's house for supper and go to the midnight service at the huge church in nearby Cannock. There would be a big choir, a lovely crib and (as I then

· A Worcestershire Christmas ·

A winter landscape near Bromsgrove – countryside still
largely unspoilt, in which the young Pat Warner was
brought up

described it) the man with the flat hat would swing the
innocents around! The smell of incense would stay in my
nostrils for days. After we left church, my aunt and uncle
would curse and argue all the way home.

Here at my aunt's I would sleep in a folding chair. I lay
awake for hours, waiting for Father Christmas to come down
the chimney. Somehow, I always missed him. I had the same
presents in my stocking each year: a large coloured play ball, a
sugar pig, an orange and one bright new shining penny.

Christmas in Wolverhampton meant more to me than
anything else in the world. For once, there would be water

from the tap by the sink; gas light in the kitchen to show me the way across the yard to the WC outside; a gas stove in the kitchen on which to boil the kettle . . . all this was achieved at the turn of a switch. The mantle in the light globe made a funny hissing sound, quite warm and homely. So different from the lamplight at Tardebigge. A gas light glowed in the street just outside the house, and friendly noises could be heard from the shunting yard at the nearby railway station.

There were always nice things to eat, with little luxuries like sago pudding. On Christmas morning it was cold boiled ham for breakfast. Uncle worked for the railway and was 'rich'. Afterwards, we dressed in our Sunday Best to attend the Christmas morning service. But first, always on a Christmas morning, without fail, my aunt would scrub the back yard. Down she went on her hands and knees and scrubbed and scrubbed. Meanwhile, my 'rich' uncle became madder and madder, shouting and blaspheming and then hoping that the Good Lord would forgive him.

If we were lucky, we might get our Christmas dinner about 3 p.m. I just couldn't wait for dinner to be cleared away because I knew that afterwards the grown-ups would play cards, so they wouldn't need me around. That could only mean one thing:

'Put little Pat into the parlour. There's a nice fire. She can amuse herself.'

A lovely fire cast its shadows on the parlour ceiling. It was the only day of the year that this room was open to the public apart from weddings and funerals. The 'holy of holies' shone brighter than the Eastern Star!

Cards finished, my uncle could settle down for the great moment he had been waiting for: a sing-song round the piano. The walls would ring with the rendering of fine old Victorian carols. My favourite was 'The Mistletoe Bough' by Thomas Haynes Bayly:

The mistletoe hung in the castle hall.
The holly branch shone on the old oak wall.
The Baron's retainers were blithe and gay
While keeping their Christmas holiday.
The Baron beheld with a fatherly pride
His beautiful child, young Lovell's bride.
She, with her bright eyes, seemed to be
The star of that goodly company.
Oh, the mistletoe bough.
Oh, the mistletoe bough.

Uncle Dick was a good pianist and that never-to-be-forgotten carol made a perfect Christmas. We went home the day after Boxing Day.

I didn't have a Christmas tree, either at home or at my aunt's. A holly bush would be hung from a large hook in the ceiling at home, provided that the home-cured bacon had first been removed. This top, taken from a holly tree, was a pretty sight, a bow of tinsel, a pink sugar pig and a white sugar mouse being the only decorations. But it filled the house with the spirit and magic of Christmas. I knew that the little pig, with his friend the mouse, would afterwards be returned to their paper wrappings for next Christmas . . . and the next . . . and the next. Eventually, they were so old, worn and dusty they were almost beyond recognition. I never knew what happened to them.

There is nothing to compare with a childhood Christmas. The waking at some unearthly hour for that wonderful moment when you looked for the presents. They were always there. The great preparations beforehand like sitting up through the night to boil the Christmas puddings in the copper. Mince pies were the size of saucers, covered in caster sugar and often washed down with a glass of Father's homemade 'poison'. It was an adventure to go tramping though the snow to gather the holly, ivy and mistletoe from some secret place. The snow was as fine and white as the

113

icing on the cake. And you must never forget to make a wish whilst stirring the Christmas puddings.

Childhood Christmas treats left a great impression on my mind. The magic of hanging up a pillow-case, the feel of the sugar pig and the orange lying hidden in one corner, and most of all that wonderful faith in Father Christmas.

Home from Wolverhampton, it was strange to lie in my own bed again and to listen to the weird sounds of the cut instead of the rattling trams going up the Cannock Road. Father, too, enjoyed these Christmas treats as much as I did. Before we went away he would read Dickens's *A Christmas Carol* to me, the story of Scrooge and the ghosts and the sad little Tiny Tim. He was probably glad to get away from our house in case he, too, might see the spirits of Christmases past.

from

A Good Christmas Box

ANON

In 1847, a collection of traditional carols under the title A Good Christmas Box *was printed and published by G. Walters of High Street, Dudley. Now valuable as a*

reference work for its source material. it contains several authentic versions of the more familiar carols. but is notable for the many lesser-known examples — like the one reproduced here — which are nevertheless delightful commentaries on the Christmas story and very much a part of the English carolling tradition.

RIGHTEOUS JOSEPH

When righteous Joseph wedded was
Unto a virtuous maid,
A glorious angel came from heaven,
And to the virgin said —

'Hail, blessed Mary, full of grace,
The Lord remains with thee.
Thou shalt conceive and bear a Son,
Man's Saviour he shall be.'

'Tis wondrous strange, quoth Mary, then,
I should conceive and breed,
Who ne'er was touched by mortal man,
In word, or thought, or deed.

When Joseph he returned
To Mary, meek and mild,
He wondered strangely at his wife
To see her big with child.

God's messenger she did believe,
And is to Jerusalem gone,
Three months with her friends to stay,
God's blessed will be done.

Thus spake the angel Gabriel,
This is not the work of man,
It is by God's ordained will,
E'er since the world began.

She's mother, maid, and married wife,
By Jesus' birth befel,
And by his power and by his grace,
He'll conquer death and hell.

O Joseph do not blame your wife,
She's still a virtuous maid;
For no consent to any sin,
Against her can be laid.

from

Cast a Long Shadow

MARY PEARCE

The largely unspoilt countryside of south Worcestershire has inspired the setting for much of Mary Pearce's writing, notably her delightful trilogy Apple Tree Saga.

116

· A Worcestershire Christmas ·

Her later book Cast a Long Shadow, *also set in Worcestershire, chronicles the chequered life of a nineteenth-century miller, Richard Lancy, his wife Ellen and their young son John. In this extract, as Christmas 1879 approaches, the relationship between Richard and Ellen is becoming increasingly strained, and John is suffering from whooping cough.*

John recovered eventually and went back to school, but two weeks later he was at home again for the Christmas holiday.

'Seems it's all holidays for you!' Richard said. 'I shall have to find you something to do.'

When the doctor sent his bill, Richard dropped it in Ellen's lap.

'You can pay that.'

'How can I?'

'I dunno how. That's up to you. I said you'd be sorry for calling him in.'

'Very well', Ellen said.

She went to Rainborough the next day and sold the cameo brooch that her Uncle John had given her on her eighteenth birthday. When she had paid the doctor's bill she still had fourteen shillings left, and she put the money into a jug on the top shelf of the dresser.

'Well?' Richard said at suppertime. 'Did you pay the doctor's bill?'

'Yes, I called at his house.'

'Where did you get the money from? Out of the week's housekeeping?'

'That goes nowhere. You should know that. I had to sell my cameo brooch.'

'You'll have a bit left over, then.'

'Yes. I thought I would buy some extras for Christmas.'

But when she went to the jug again her money was gone,

and when she spoke to Richard about it he merely shrugged.

'It came in handy, that fourteen shillings. Say I borrowed it as a loan. I'll pay it back when business gets better, though when that'll be it's hard to say.'

Whereas in the past he had wanted the best for his wife and son, now he grudged every penny she spent. John's clothes had to be turned, and his boots had to be bought second-hand. Even food was difficult, for Richard grumbled at the amount of flour she used and doled it out to her, so much a week, never allowing her into the mealroom. He gave her no extra money for Christmas and if Jerry Trussler had not called as always, bringing a twelve-pound goose, they would have had no Christmas dinner.

'I've got no money for extras,' Richard said. 'This has been a bad old year. You must manage as best you can.'

'You've got money to spend on brandy,' she said, 'but none to buy your son a present.'

'The boy is spoilt enough already. He's getting too full of hisself by half.'

Christmas that year was the saddest Ellen had ever known. There was no softening in Richard's manner; no show of cheerfulness for the child's sake; nothing to set the day apart except what she herself could contrive. Richard went to the mill as usual and spent the morning tarring the luccomb. He was up at the top of a ladder when a few people from Water Lane passed on their way to the church in Dingham.

'Don't you know what day it is, Mr Lancy?'

'Yes, it's Thursday!' Richard said.

Ellen, in the kitchen, cooking dinner, gave John little tasks to do and tried to create a festive feeling. She got him to climb on a high stool and hang sprigs of holly on the beams. She gave him the apples to peel for sauce. She allowed him to baste the roasting goose, growing brown and crisp-skinned in the oven of the range. He was happy enough in his quiet way, until his father came in to dinner.

Richard as usual had little to say. When he did speak, it was only to grumble at the church bells, ringing in Dingham and Sutton Crabtree and three miles away in the abbey at Rainborough.

'They've been at it all morning and that's a noise I can't abide. Dothering, dothering, in my head, all the time I was up that ladder. The ringers must want something to do!'

'It *is* Christmas, after all.'

'D'you think I don't know?'

Ellen, talking cheerfully, remarked on the tenderness of the goose.

'Aren't we lucky,' she said to John, 'that Mr Trussler should be so kind, giving us a goose at Christmastime?'

'Kind? Why kind?' Richard said. 'I reckon he owes me something, don't he, seeing I gave him one of my donkeys to carry on his smelly trade?'

That afternoon, when Richard had shut himself in the mill, Ellen and John sat in the kitchen and roasted chestnuts at the fire. The nuts were small. She had picked them up in the woods at Spinnam. When they popped open and flew out into the hearth, John laughed and clapped his hands. But then, suddenly, even as he laughed, his small face crumpled and he was in tears. Sobs shook him. He bowed his head. Ellen took him in her arms.

'Don't cry, don't cry,' she said to him. 'Why, I was going to sing some carols! Favourites of yours, like "The First Nowell", and I shall need you to tell me the words. What about "I Saw Two Ships"? You know how I get in a muddle with that. How can I sing it without your help?'

'*Three* ships,' he said, drawing back to frown at her.

'Three? Are you sure?' And she wiped his eyes. 'I do believe you're right,' she said. 'But where were they sailing to, those three ships?'

'Everybody knows that!'

· A Worcestershire Christmas ·

Mary Pearce: the south Worcestershire countryside inspired
much of her writing

'I suppose they were sailing to Sutton Crabtree.'

'Silly!' he said. 'It was Bethlehem.'

'There! I told you I always got in a muddle. What a good
thing it is that you know the words.'

But although she could comfort him in the end, and even
bring back the laughter again, secretly she was afraid. What of
next Christmas? she asked herself. What would their lives be
like by then?

After Christmas, the weather worsened. 1880 came in cold.
There were several days of hard frost. One morning, when

Richard had some beans to grind, the waterwheel was frozen up. He laid a plank from the footbridge to the wheel, resting it on the edge of a paddle, and went across with a big kettle of boiling water, to thaw the ice surrounding the axle. But the axle, frozen, had warped a little, and the waterwheel, after less than a quarter turn, caught against the mill wall. Richard, swearing angrily, put the plank across again and set to work with hammer and chisel.

It was not easy for him to reach from the plank, and he was about to climb up the wheel when he saw John watching him from the garden.

'Ent you got nothing better to do than stand there gawping at me?' he said. But when the boy would have turned away, Richard called him back again. 'Come round here. You can give me a hand. You're a lot smaller and lighter than me. This here job is just right for you.'

Half an hour later, Ellen, going in search of John, found him crouched on the waterwheel, struggling with hammer and cold chisel, chipping at the brickwork of the wall where the rim of the wheel had caught against it. Richard, on the plank, was peering between the wheel and the wall, shouting instructions, but the little boy, his hands blue with cold, could scarcely lift the heavy tools and more often than not the blows of the hammer went astray.

'Lord Almighty!' Richard said. 'Can't you do no better than that? Get the chisel against that brick and keep tapping until it chips.'

'I can't!' John said, with a little sob. 'I can't do it! It's too hard. I shall drop the hammer in a minute.'

'You do, that's all, and see what happens!'

Ellen ran forward on to the bridge and cried out to Richard to bring the boy down. He glanced at her over his shoulder and muttered something under his breath. Then he turned to the boy again and put up his arms.

'You may as well come down, I suppose, for all the use you are up there! Come on, come on, I ent got all day! You'll have to come down further'n that or I can't reach you.'

Inch by inch, the boy moved towards him. Crouched as he was on the ice-covered paddles, he was terrified that the wheel would move and that he would be borne down into the stream, where the swift white water ran full pelt. He was paralysed with cold. His fingers were stiffened, twisted like claws, clutching the heavy hammer and chisel.

Richard took hold of him, under the armpits, and carried him back along the plank. He swung him over the rail of the bridge into Ellen's waiting arms.

'Here, take your chilver, he's no use to me! I'll have to do the job myself.' He snatched the tools from John's hands and turned towards the waterwheel. 'He don't even try to help me, that boy. All he does is snivel and cry.'

'He might have been drowned!' Ellen exclaimed, pressing the child against her body. 'Supposing the wheel had begun to turn? Have you got no sense at all?'

'The wheel wouldn't shift as fast as that. If it had I'd have tumbled in myself.'

'The boy is frozen through to the bone. Have you no feeling left for him? Can't you see him suffering?'

'Then get him into the house, woman, instead of standing there ranting at me! And take that empty kettle with you. I've finished with it for today.'

Ellen left him and went indoors. She put John to sit in a chair by the stove and wrapped her shawl around his shoulders. Now and then a shiver shook him, but he was quite silent and sat in a trance, staring into the heart of the fire. When she spoke he seemed not to hear her. His face was shuttered, unreadable, the eyelids drooping, hiding the eyes, the lashes shadowing the pallid cheeks. He was shut up inside himself. Even she could not reach him.

from

A Haircut and a Shave

PHILIP GREEN

Although he described his autobiography, written in 1974 after he had retired as a director of a Midland engineering firm, as that of a 'nonentity', Philip Green nevertheless tells the story of a full and varied life reflecting a period of great social and political change. Born into Edwardian England and educated at Malvern College, he served in the Royal Air Force in the Second World War and spent his latter years at Suckley near Worcester. Some of his most vivid recollections concern his childhood, and in this extract he casts his mind back to a typical family Christmas.

Two annual events varied the pattern of the holidays. One was Christmas; the other, the annual visit to the seaside.

Christmas, I suppose was then much as it is now except that it was more restricted in time. By this I mean that it was not a preoccupation for months beforehand. The shops did not begin a seasonal display until December was well under way. Nowadays we seem to find it necessary to start worrying about the purchase of gifts months beforehand if we are to get a reasonable variety of choice. Father, after a good lunch at his club, made all his Christmas purchases on Christmas Eve. Christmas cards were posted to arrive on Christmas Day, when the postman would make several appearances.

Mother liked to ensure that we all had bulging pillowcases at the foot of our beds. She would wrap up miscellaneous objects, which had lain about the house for years, to swell the number of our presents. There was annual speculation as to who would get the copy of *Our Sailor King*, which never failed to appear.

Perhaps the season was a little less secular than it is now. Everyone went to church – except the cook! Cocktail parties were unheard of; indeed, so were cocktails. No one visited; it was a strictly family affair. It was, of course, perhaps to an even greater extent than today, frankly an almighty blowout. The traditional turkey and plum pudding and the more exotic fruits such as pineapples, tangerines, figs and dates made their only appearance of the year.

Boxing Day, as now, saw the start of the pantomime season, for us the only theatrical event of the year. I have not seen a pantomime for years, but I gather they have not altered much. The humour might be a bit broader, but I doubt it. George Robey could be relied on to pop in something here and there to compensate the attendant adults for doing their duty by the children. The audience was primarily childish. There were no mass bookings for works' parties or coach loads from the Women's Institute, which today drag out the pantomime season for months, to the exclusion of any other form of stage entertainment in the provinces.

Philip Green chose the title of his autobiography from a verse written by Samuel Hoffenstein.

Babies haven't any hair
Old men's heads are just as bare.
Between the cradle and the grave
Lies a haircut and a shave.

Festive Fare

ROLAND TITMUS

Looking at Christmas recipes of any age can be a mouth-watering experience, and early examples can make fascinating reading, especially when compared with those of today which rely largely on pre-packed ingredients from the supermarket, and the ever-present freezer and micro-wave. In 1981, Roland Titmus gleaned these seasonal secrets from the great kitchens of historic country houses in and around Worcestershire.

Not surprisingly, there is an abundance of game dishes among the early recipes, although the one for 'Breast of Pheasant Hagley', mentioned by Viscountess Cobham of Hagley Hall is of more recent origin. You require two pheasants, ½ lb of lard, 4 bacon slices, ½ gill of port, juice of ½ lemon, ½ oz chopped shallots, 1 pint of brown stock, 1 oz of flour, 4 slices

of bread, 2 ozs of game pâté, 1 tin of asparagus tips, ½ a teaspoon of English mustard, ½ lb of redcurrant jelly, ½ a gill of orange juice, the zest of 1 orange, and seasoning.

'Roast the pheasants in the usual way,' says the recipe, 'and remove the breast from the carcase and keep warm. Drain off the fat from the roasting-tin, leaving a little to make a thickened gravy. Melt the redcurrant jelly, add the mustard and whisk in the port and orange juice. Shallow fry the shallots and add to the gravy with the jelly mixture. Reduce the sauce by half and strain.

'Fry the bread or toast it, and spread with the pâté. Place the pheasant breasts on the bread, mask with the sauce, lay the asparagus tips on top and sprinkle with the orange zest.'

Lord Sandys of Ombersley Court near Droitwich contributes Ombersley Pie which was served to guests at luncheon sixty or seventy years ago.

The ingredients are 2 dozen sauce oysters, 2 lb of beefsteak, 1 tablespoon of flour, 1 level teaspoon of salt, the same of pepper, 1 yolk of an egg, beef stock, chopped parsley, puff pastry or short-crust pastry.

The recipe continues: 'Cut the meat into thin slices, about

three inches in length and width. Beard the oysters and blanch the beards in the oyster liquor which must be reheated, seasoned, strained and added to the gravy in the pie just before serving. Place an oyster on each slice of meat and roll up tightly. Mix the flour, salt and pepper together on a plate, dip the rolls of meat in the mixture and place them on end in a pie dish. Sprinkle the rest of the seasoning mixture, together with the chopped parsley, between the layers of meat. Pour in enough beef stock to three-quarters fill the dish. Make the paste and roll out to a suitable thickness. Lay a border round the edge of the pie dish, and, having wetted it, cover the pie with a covering of the same paste, pressing the edges well together. Make a hole in the centre of the top and brush over the surface with the yolk of an egg. The pie must now be baked in a hot oven until the paste has risen and set. Afterwards it should be cooked more slowly – up to two hours in all. Before serving, pour in through the hole in the top the oyster liquor which has already been prepared as above.'

'It seems to have been very popular,' Lord Sandys tells me, 'since we still hear about it in the reminiscences of an earlier generation.'

Or you might prefer Wightwick Party Flapjacks, which Lady Mander of Wightwick Manor, on the edge of the Black Country, tells me she acquired 'from one of our helpers'. You need 6 oz of butter, 6 oz of demerara sugar, 6 oz of mixed fruit (currants, raisins, cherries, angelica, and a few walnuts if wished), 8 oz of rolled oats, a pinch of salt, plain or milk chocolate.

'Melt the fat in a saucepan over gentle heat, mix in the sugar, oats and salt, stir well, and add the fruit. Put into a well-greased tin or flan dish, press well down and smooth over with a knife. Bake for about 35 minutes, and when cooked golden brown, remove from the oven, break the chocolate into small pieces and put on top while still hot. Cut into squares and leave in the tin to get cold before removing.'

'Minced pies' in a Worcestershire recipe book from the secluded mansion of Shakenhurst, to the west of Bewdley, closely resemble those of today, though the dishes are of the eighteenth and nineteenth centuries. But I do have a 'receipt' for 'Ragout Pigs' Ears' attributed to Mrs Lechmere in a manuscript book lent to me by Sir Berwick Lechmere Bart of Severn End at Hanley Castle near Upton-upon-Severn.

'Take the thin part of the ear (cut it into narrow bits about the bigness of a straw). Have ready a good gravy. Boil it up in that and thicken it with butter or flour. Just as you send it to table, squeeze in a little walnut pickle, katchup or lemon juice, whichever you prefer.'

I think I'd rather have those party flapjacks.

The Christmas Tree

MEINRAD CRAIGHEAD

In 1966 Meinrad Craighead, an American nun, entered Stanbrook Abbey, the Benedictine nunnery near Worcester. Here she found time to explore her talents as an artist, and a few years later she produced, in book form, a collection of her scraper-board drawings depicting the deep symbolism

· A Worcestershire Christmas ·

Meinrad Craighead's symbolic representation of the
Christmas tree

she saw in trees. She called it The Sign of the Tree *and,
inevitably, included in its pages this detailed description
and illustration of the symbolic significance of the Christmas tree.*

Many ancient peoples all over the world celebrated the low
solar observances at midwinter with sacred light and fire
liturgies. In the Mediterranean world, important festivities
centred around the Roman Saturnalia, which began on
December 17th, and the birthday of the Iranian god Mithra,
which was celebrated on December 25th. Homes and temples
were illuminated with lights and fires and decorated with
branches of evergreen, the symbol of life everlasting.

This festive period at the end of the year was introduced into
Christianity in the fourth century, and Christmas – the word is
derived from the old English *Christes maesse*, Christ's mass –

became the birthday of the true *Sol Novus*, the New Sun, which would never set because Christ was also *Sol Invictus*, the victor over the forces of darkness and death.

In northern Europe in the Middle Ages, the evergreen tree, a universal tree of life symbol, was decorated with candles and bread, and gifts were exchanged around the flaming yule log. Garlands of green leaves protected man and beast against the powers of evil which were believed to be strongest at the midwinter Dark of Year when the old sun was weakest.

Even in today's urban societies the Christmas tree is the vestigial 'sacred tree', brought into the home, fêted, decorated, and placed at the centre of the season. Around it Christians still celebrate the archetypal drama of light victorious over darkness.

Carols, Cockerels and Christmas Cheer

FRED ARCHER

In this fourth extract of Fred Archer's seasonal jottings, he looks back at some of the customs which contributed to the spirit of Christmas in his home village. They may seem

· A Worcestershire Christmas ·

remarkably simple and unsophisticated when compared with the way we celebrate Christmas today, but were an indelible part of the air of excitement which young and old alike experienced during this annual highspot in the rural calendar.

Back in the 1920s Christmas started for us in our village of Ashton-under-Hill on St Thomas's Day, 21 December. Early on St Thomas's morning, well before daylight on the shortest day, children came to the door chanting or singing: 'Here we come a'Thomasing, a'Thomasing, a'Thomasing; Here we come a'Thomasing, so early in the morning'. This kind of carol was sung to collect pennies from the village folk.

In the neighbouring parish of Beckford, 21 December was Mumping Day. Mumping is a polite term for begging, and it was the women from the nearby hamlet of Grafton who came to Beckford to do it. They called at the big houses of the farmers and would recite traditional verses. With the money collected from Mumping, the women and children bought blankets from a Mr Smith of Smith's Stores who offered them for sale in the school room.

Christmas Day itself began with the carol singers and the Tewkesbury drum and fife band coming round the village. They played just one carol, 'Oh Come All Ye Faithful' and were known as the Tabber and Tut band. They were compared unfavourably with the Salvation Army band who also came to play in the village street. To hear the Salvationists on a crisp frosty night was magic.

In the days when the men of the land had no paid holidays, they always looked forward eagerly to Christmas Day. The village boys shinned up apple trees cutting sprigs of mistletoe, and the cottage doors and windows were hung with laurel, ivy and yew branches. The furnace in the washroom no longer boiled the sheets and shirts, but Christmas puddings. They

131

An early photograph of Fred Archer and his daughter
Shelagh feeding their Dorset Horn ewes and tending winter-
born lambs

simmered away for hours in pudding basins covered with
cloths tied down with string.

No-one mentioned chicken dinners in those days. Instead,
like other families, we had something much more grand, a
cockerel. It was usually a cross-bred Rhode Island Red Light
Sussex fed on boiled potatoes and sharps.

Ponto, who lived rough in the carthouse, would sing 'Wild
Shapperds Watch', and one Christmas my mother asked him
into our kitchen to give him a plate of Christmas fare and a
bowl of jelly. Ponto said, 'I'd like some more of that shaky
stuff Ma'm.' He had another helping and wished us all a happy
Christmas.

There are some wonderful tales of carol singers years ago. In a neighbouring village there was a brass band and they always played carols at Christmas. The bandsmen were well-primed with home-made wine, and plum jerkum in particular, and on one occasion they played two carols outside what they thought was someone's cottage. It was only when they couldn't find the door that they realised the 'cottage' was a neatly thatched hayrick in a farmer's yard. It took them a long time to live that episode down.

Our local bell-ringers were the best carol singers. They sang their Christmas pieces by the light of a hurricane lamp hung on a bean pole. Ralph, our carter, was one of them, and he would knock on the farmhouse door and whisper: 'Be the little 'uns gone to bed?' I heard him because I was one of the little 'uns!

'No,' Dad said. 'Then we'll sing you a couple Master,' Ralph replied.

They struck up 'While Shepherds Watched Their Flocks By Night', a rustic choir of men's voices, but it was real Christmas music.

Frank Whittle, one of the ringers, walked on crutches. He had lost a leg in France in the Great War. Despite his disability he was a great walker and could always be seen following the Croome Hounds on one leg after Christmas. I once went with him on one of these occasions, and it was all I could do to keep up with him as he took massive strides on his crutches. Frank was the best singer in the bell-ringers' choir. His mellow rich voice reminded me of Paul Robeson.

Charlie Moore, a hurdle-maker, was captain of the tower, and he would always lead the men in one of the old Ashton carols before they went on their way. This was 'All Hail and Praise the Sacred Morn'. The younger carol singers would be perfectly satisfied if they were rewarded with a bag of oranges or apples and pennies.

Our village could just as well have been a moated castle. No-one left at Christmas and very few folk came. There was a

feeling of self-sufficiency. Christmas fostered a real community spirit which existed all the year.

The dark nights meant time by the fireside playing dominoes, cards or various games. We learned as children to use the things around us for pleasure. When the pig was killed the bladder was blown up; that was our balloon. The old drill wheels off the farm were our hoops, and we played tip cat and whip tops.

These were the early days of the wireless, and Christmas was not complete without listening to Bransbury Williams as Scrooge in *A Christmas Carol* by Dickens.

The great difference between Christmas today and that of the 1920s is that all those years ago the festive season didn't begin until a few days before the 25th. Nowadays it begins in October.

A Christmas Greeting

C. ALICE ELGAR

Shortly before Christmas in 1907, Sir Edward Elgar and his wife, Caroline Alice, journeyed from Worcestershire to Rome. While they were there, Lady Elgar wrote this carol and addressed it to 'Dr Sinclair and the choristers of Hereford Cathedral' as a contribution to their Christmas concert of carols.

134

· A Worcestershire Christmas ·

Caroline Alice Elgar, wife of the great Worcestershire
composer

I

Bowered on sloping hillside rise
In sunny glow, the purpling vine;
Beneath the greyer English skies,
In fair array, the red-gold apples shine.
To those in snow,
To those in sun,
Love is but one;
Hearts beat and glow
By oak or palm
Friends, in storm or calm.

II

On and on old Tiber speeds,
Dark with the weight of ancient crime;
Far north, through green and quiet meads,
Flows on the Wye in mist and silvering rime.
To those in snow, etc.

III

The pifferari wander far,
They seek the shrines, and hymn the peace
Which herald angels, 'neath the star,
Foretold to shepherds, bidding strife to cease.
To those in snow, etc.

IV

Our England sleeps in shroud of snow,
Bells, sadly sweet, knell life's swift flight,
And tears, unbid, are wont to flow,
As 'Noel! Noel!' sounds across the night.
To those in snow, etc.

C. ALICE ELGAR
Rome, Dec 1907

Christmas Has Never Been the Same

CHARLES LINES

Back in the 1920s, long before the intrusive dominance of Christmas by radio and television, the celebrations had a special magic of their own. Commercialism, too, had yet to assert itself, and the festive season still enjoyed an air of sincerity and simplicity. Writer and historian Charles Lines, whose family's roots are deeply implanted in Worcestershire, has recorded these memories of the traditional Christmases of his childhood.

The old-fashioned Christmas may have been on its way out – probably it always was – but, perhaps because Father was a Worcestershire man, born and bred, and averse to change for its own sake, he insisted that the festive season should be celebrated in true, traditional style.

I won't say he welcomed the advent of carol singers with their renderings of 'Goo King Wenslus' and hammerings on the door, and he was decidedly put out when, having bestowed a shilling on an itinerant brass band, he discovered that the musicians were spending their ill-gotten gains in a nearby hostelry.

Other folk were more fortunate. The 'Postman's Christmas Box', for instance, was quite a different matter. The two men – always two – who came after dark with an oil lamp, were well rewarded in the immediate aftermath of the First World War. After all, we then had three deliveries on weekdays, as well as one on Sundays and even on Christmas Day, and the poor chaps' wages were about as negligible as the price of stamps.

Christmas, of course, was spent at home – no hotels, let alone the ski slopes of Austria – and it entailed, I now realise, a vast amount of hard work for Mother, though domestic help was plentiful and inexpensive. Preparations, however, didn't begin with the sales of the previous January, and I doubt if pantomime tickets were advertised at midsummer.

One early task was the making of 'the puddings', always from the same old family recipe.

Half-a-dozen brimming basins were tied up with cloth and immersed in the big scullery copper. About the same time, jars of home-made mincemeat appeared on pantry shelves, and a Christmas cake – Mother would never have bought one – was secreted in its tin box. No-one thought twice about tasks like the stoning of raisins, the shredding of suet and candied peel, and grating of nutmeg, which are unknown in many a home today.

As time went on, there was much confabulation with the grocer's traveller, who received a glass of port ('Thank you, Ma'am; the compliments of the season Ma'am') just prior to the great day, but, looking back, I marvel how self-contained we were. The orchard gave us such delights as russet apples and little rosy-red favourites whose name I never heard, to mix with nuts and oranges and sticky dates, in case anybody was hungry between meals. There were big pears too – hard as rock when dangerously gathered from our tall trees, but deliciously mellow by the time they were wanted for the essential dessert.

· *A Worcestershire Christmas* ·

The custom of carol singing has survived all the vicissitudes
of Christmas celebrations over the years

Needless to say, we had no freezer, but the kitchen garden
yielded every vegetable we needed, including fat, succulent
sprouts and giant parsnips, apart from the onions and herbs to
accompany whatever poultry we chose.

The choice of poultry was a matter for great debate, and I
remember once we had suckling pig. It wasn't a huge success.
Somehow we felt that the poor thing had lost its life too early,
even if its larger brethren, contentedly grunting on our farm
until the well-oiled pig-killer deigned to make an appearance,
elicited no sympathy. Yes, we had home-cured bacon to baste
the bird, and there was pork for the stand-up pies, so
beautifully seasoned and quite different from the sort the 'lazy
folk' bought in the shops.

139

· A Worcestershire Christmas ·

Milk lay in wide pans in the dairy, ready to be delicately skimmed for the festive trifle, and for the butter made in a hand-turned glass churn that would be a museum-piece today. Featherweight little cakes and a regiment of mince pies made with flaky pastry reposed on wire trays, sometimes 'mysteriously' disappearing before their time. A special claret cup was made to serve in green glasses which I still have to this day.

Curiously, we rarely had a Christmas tree, but the house was well decorated with holly from the farm, and with paper festoons and tinsel and Chinese lanterns from the big chest on the upper landing.

On Christmas morning, the old kitchen range, scrupulously black-leaded by 'Mrs T.', who had half-a-crown for hours of work that included scrubbing and a huge wash, glowed beautifully.

Guests were not welcome if they arrived too soon. It was wise to absent oneself at church while the turkey was roasted; some folk including 'Auntie' were apt to offer culinary advice that was not appreciated.

Fires had to be blazing in the dining room and drawing room, the table extended, the special cloth (an heirloom from an inn-keeping forbear) laid, and the silver carefully placed, before any knock on the door. Once, before my day, there had been twenty-four or more at midday, involving two sittings. Later, partly I fear because of Great Aunt Sarah's will, numbers had dwindled to a mere twelve or fifteen, headed by grandparents who looked like grandparents.

Dinner was followed by a certain somnolence and scent of cigars, accompanied by some talk of farming and the sad state of the country. The more energetic sometimes fancied a walk over our fields, taking in a visit to calves in dark pens and an inspection of ricks.

A fairly late tea – with crackers, the splendid trifle, quivering jellies and the best Crown Derby – was followed by a move to the drawing room. Sometimes, I'm asked what we did before the days of television or even the crystal set with headphones. Entertainment was home-made, like the cake, aided by a hand-wound gramophone. I often wonder now why the songs were so melancholy; they always seemed to be about sailors asleep in the deep, or trumpeters in battle, although we never got as far as 'Close the Shutters, Millie's Dead!' 'Auntie' was certain to render 'Thora' and I regret to say I recited.

The warm fire and the closed curtains obliterated gloomy thoughts, and the occasional ghost story was just a thrill. We sometimes played simple games – no cards though, if Christmas Day was on a Sunday – and we indulged in conjuring that certainly wouldn't have impressed Paul Daniels. There was late-night dancing, too, on the quarried floor of the kitchen, that was quite different from the odd antics that pass for dancing nowadays.

Perhaps the greatest joy, however, was Boxing Day, dipping into books and eating left-overs, and thankful that an unpopular uncle hadn't appeared after all!

It was all a long time ago. The fields where we once roamed have now gone, making way for houses in which people now spend their Christmases huddled over videos – and have never tasted a *real* pork pie.

from

Kidderminster Since 1800

KEN TOMKINSON AND GEORGE HALL

Both George Hall and the late Ken Tomkinson shared a common interest in Kidderminster's local history, and they both worked in the carpet industry. Tomkinson was also a publisher, and Hall is an archivist and writer. In 1975 they collaborated on Kidderminster Since 1800, *which includes this evocative account of pre-Christmas shopping and a festive family gathering in mid-Victorian times.*

There were plenty of local shops catering for the elegance of the ladies. Southan and Company advertised their new silk room, opening for shawls, silks, furs and cloaks. Michael Tomkinson in the High Street returned from a purchasing mission to London, Manchester and Leeds, and drew attention to his immense stock of shawls, silks, furs, cloaks, merinos, woollen cloths, Cassimeres, milled broads, petershams, ribbons, lace, hose, gloves, flannels, blankets, counterpanes and furniture, all equally cheap. The local ladies were well served for lace, for Miss Standish, the lace worker of Bewdley Street, had won both a medal and a plate at the great exhibition.

Proportionately, perhaps, more social life took place in the privacy of the home, and a family gathering would be normal on all significant occasions. With the large families of the time, the following record of 1846, showing twenty-one people present, would not be abnormal. It is extracted from a record in prose and verse relating to the Lea family of Kidderminster.

A family Christmas festival was held at their home in Blakebrook on 26th December 1846. The centre of events was the German tree, standing in its flower pot about 9 feet high. The lower branches were tied up, and the space formed on one side into a grotto, and the other a fairy palace, with walls of looking glass, pillars of barley sugar, and a pavement of variegated sugar plums. The other branches were hung with gilded eggs, bells, artificial fruit, flowers, grapes in silver baskets, and dolls, all surmounted by flags, and illuminated by coloured tapers. The family group assembled in the drawing room about 4 p.m., and proceeded to a lengthy, detailed and admirative examination of the tree and its decorations.

Games such as hunt the slipper were then played, while the tree was hung with twenty-one coloured purses, which were distributed to the participants. While the audience again played games in the drawing room, the tree was redecorated. The party now proceeded to the special ceremonial of the annual coronation of dear uncle's bust, after which followed many country dances such as 'Sir Roger de Coverley'.

from

Come Rain, Come Shine

JOHN MOORE

John Moore wrote Come Rain, Come Shine *in 1956 as a successor to* The Season of the Year, *and once again he reviews the seasonal pleasures of rural England, inspired by the unspoilt countryside where Worcestershire meets Gloucestershire. In this extract he contemplates Christmas in prose and verse.*

And now the first Christmas cards are on the mantelpiece, not only the arty ones from the people who hold representational robins in contempt, but the stage-coaches and the yule logs and the old-world cottages iced with snow. Christmas wouldn't be quite Christmas without its vulgarities: 'Good King Wenceslas' made up by J.M. Neal in 1855 and now sung at the front door by nice little children with horrid little voices; the bauble-decorated spruce brought to England by Albert the Good ('who also introduced fish knives'); a sentimentalised saint from Germany, a turkey from the Americas, a kiss under the mistletoe which solemn folklorists derive from the Druidical sacrifice of virgins, and an indigestible pudding which only a heavy-handed English cook could have devised!

We must have the lot; *and* the biggest mistletoe bough in the whole orchard, which generally grows at the top of the tallest apple tree, so that I shall need the forty-rung ladder to cut it down. Striving in vain to hold this ladder upright as I carry it towards the tree, I feel like a sea-lion balancing a walking-stick on the end of its nose. Then comes the holly-gathering and the last-minute decorating (for, unac-countably, the seasons creeping upon us always take us by surprise). But at last we're ready; and it's Christmas Day.

There's a kind of nadir between tea and dinner on Christmas Day, when time inexplicably ceases, and clocks tick without meaning, and somehow nothing is quite real. Everybody experiences this phenomenon, nobody can explain it. But it is curiously enjoyable. *Pickwick* is the book to read then; or one can tell ghost stories.

Pickwick or ghost stories, no matter which; we shall yawn contentedly and Candy will sit prim and yawning before the fire, forgetting how last night under the wild moon she was compounded of tiger, witch and devil, nor apprehending that in a few hours she will be so again. It is a time for smugness, for which we all possess our share. The wind should therefore howl loudly in the chimney. Let it blow its cheeks out.

And just before six o'clock, when we switch on the wireless to hear the news, there should be gale warnings, and the level voice of the announcer should speak to us the names of the sea-areas bluff and salt-sounding, pandering to our smugness and the sense of security engendered by thick walls. Lundy, Dogger, Cromarty, Humber, Heligoland; perhaps if I hadn't spent some wartime Christmases bucketing round about them I shouldn't dare to feel so smug! But they are poetry however you string them together; you can hear the surge of the sea and the roar of the wind in them. So while the wind is loud in the

'An indigestible pudding which only a heavy-handed
English cook could have devised!'

chimney and the great words are still blustering through my
mind, I try to match some verses to my mood:

Draw close the curtains. (Mares' Tails streaking the night sky
And looks like rain?)
With the wireless going, you won't notice the creeper
Rat-tatting on the pane.
Shut out the night with its wild whispering voices,
Its cries and its calls,
The tempestuous world kept at bay with your solid
Inviolate walls.
So settle down to a peaceful finish to Christmas.
Kick off your shoes;
Cherry-logs merrily crackling, a drink at your elbow,

Time for the News.
Cat on the hearth, book on your lap, and suddenly over the air,
Out of the void, into your quiet,
Come the great sea-names that roar and riot,
Humber, Lundy, Faroes, Forties, Fastnet, Forth and
Finisterre!

Tendril of creeper beats a tattoo on the window
Like a limed linnet.
Know now that you live on an island! – Your house is
An island within it!
The pitiless winds of the world all about you; and surging
Into your room
Comes the heave and the sigh and the crash of the steep
Atlantic,
The spray and the spume.
The fire leaps high, and harshly the dry logs sputter.
The wind has risen!
The chimney always smokes when it's in that quarter. . . .
Islander, listen:
As the cat gets up and your book falls shut, and suddenly over
the air,
Out of the void, into your quiet,
Come the great sea-names that roar and riot,
Humber, Lundy, Faroes, Forties, Fastnet, Forth and
Finisterre!

Wassailing the Winter Orchards

Many and varied were the seasonal customs associated with the land in days gone by. Wassailing the fruit trees at Christmastime was one of these, and this account by a member of the Worcestershire Naturalists' Club in Victorian times, appears in a record of the club's activities for the period from 1847 to 1896.

The sun shining on particular days was always, time out of mind, a favourite rural notion as regards good luck, and it is still a prevalent idea that if the sun shines through the apple trees of the orchards on Christmas Day, there will be an abundant crop of apples the following year.

The chief observance connected with apple orchards was that of wassailing the trees, the term derived from the Saxon *waes hael* (water of health), and thus the wassail or health-bowl became a popular institution.

This wassailing the fruit trees is a custom derived from very old times, and was observed by farmers of the last century. I have met with persons who have been at its celebration in rural districts, and I have received reliable information of its observance last Christmas.

The following account has been given me of the wassailing as witnessed some years since at a farm on the banks of the Teme in this county. The eve of the Twelfth Day, or Old

Christmas Eve, was the time observed for this rural festivity, which was originally intended to secure a blessing to the fruits of the earth, but at last the superstitious idea was taken up, that if the wassailing was omitted, the produce of the orchards would be very little. This injunction was, therefore, generally borne in mind, repeated, and acted upon:

> Wassail the trees that they may bear
> You many an apple and many a pear;
> Or more or less fruit they will bring
> As you do give them wassailing.

Therefore, on the evening mentioned, the farmer with his neighbours being assembled, they proceeded to an elevated wheat field, where twelve small fires were lighted, and a large one in the centre, these fires being generally considered as representative of our Saviour and the twelve apostles, though in some places they bear the vulgar appellation of Old Meg and her daughters.

Jugs of prime old cider having been brought, healths are joyously drunk with abundant hurrahing from a circle formed round the central fire. The party afterwards adjourn to an orchard, and there encircling one of the best bearing trees, and not forgetting cider, sprinkle the tree, while one of the party carols forth the following verse:

Here's to thee, old apple tree,
Whence thou may'st bud, and whence thou may'st blow,
And whence thou may'st bear apples enow,
Hats full and caps full,
Bushels full and sacks full,
And my pockets full too.

A chorus of obstreperous huzzas follows, and the whole

· *A Worcestershire Christmas* ·

The snow-capped Malvern Hills seen across the Teme valley.
Wassailing the orchards in this traditional fruit-growing
country was once a regular custom on Twelfth Day, or old
Christmas Eve

party then returns to the farmhouse, where a bountiful supper
with libations of cider, the result of former wassailing, awaits
them.

That this observance is not yet given up in some secluded
places is evident from what I have heard of an old farmer, who
stated to a visitor that his neglect of wassailing one year caused
the failure of his crop of apples!

Pear trees, of course, take the benefit of the wassailing
process jointly with the apple, so that except historically there
are but few things to be gathered referable to the pear alone. A
variety may, however, be mentioned, called 'the bloody pear',

from its sanguine coloured pulp when cut into, and I was once told that an orchard on the ground where the Battle of Evesham was fought, would only produce this 'bloody pear'!

Come, let us hye and quaff a cheery bowl,
Let cider now wash sorrow from the soul!

If such a panacea for the cares and sorrows of life can be accepted, the cider-cup must be considered deserving of general approval, and in thus offering it, I trust the orchards may have an abundant crop of fruit.

The Long Hard Winter

W. EILEEN DAVIES

This descriptive account comes from Seechem Chronicles, *the story of a late-Victorian and Edwardian farming family living in the Worcestershire village of Rowney Green. Although the main characters, John and Victoria Yeoman and their children, have fictional names, they are based on a real-life family who lived at Seechem, the historic farmhouse known today as Seechem Manor. In this episode, John and Victoria, with their children Spenser, Edmund and Madeline, and their young living-in maid*

· A Worcestershire Christmas ·

Bella, are faced with the sort of winter crisis which could — and often did — dominate the festive season.

The morning after his fourteenth birthday Spenser was shaken out of his sleep by a very brisk Victoria. 'Come, lad, get up quickly, do. Your father wants you.'

Spenser was not pleased. It was barely light and his bed was warm and comfortable. 'Gotter go to school. Can't work *and* go to school.' he muttered. 'Edmund can do it.'

'Edmund is already up. He's with your father and Jack now, clearing snow from the yard. It's so deep they can't reach the stables. Or the pigsty. Or the cow house. And your father is worried about the sheep, particularly your Welsh Black who looks like lambing early.'

Spenser opened his eyes.

'Get up quick as you can, Spenser, there'll be no school today. You won't be able to get there. Put on everything you can to keep warm and see if you can reach the fold in Claypit.'

The day before, a Sunday, John had enlisted the assistance of everyone on the farm, lodgers included, for the erection of a sheepfold. He had always believed in being prepared for changes in the weather and there had been distinct signs of severe conditions ahead. Everyone — including Bella who had been with them since a few weeks after the summer outing — had been out collecting fallen branches brought down by a black tempest from the north. Logs had been dragged along and brushwood reached for with hands that had refused to grow warm with exercise.

Claypit Field was named after the deep dry pit near the brow of the ridge from which marl had been dug and sold in days past. It was now mostly used by the young folk in the summer when they slid down the dry clay banks on boots and bottoms, just for the sheer joy of it. Victoria was not so joyful: clay-stained garments showed up in the wash, and boots too soon needed the repairer's attention. In the winter when the snow came they used those same slopes to toboggan down. The field was just beyond the orchard, easily and quickly reached in normal conditions, the pit westward-facing and not only quite dry but surrounded on all sides by a natural windbreak of trees.

With the wind tearing at what they held in their hands, the workers had built there a shelter for the sheep, using the growing trees as bastions. Every available old sack had been searched out from all the odd corners on the farm, torn across and pegged into the brushwood. The men and lads had fetched pitchforks full of straw and liberally strewn it on the ground; a water trough had been hauled in and filled; and quantities of hay and swedes had been dropped into the pit for food. Everything ready, the sheep had been rounded up from the field where wisely they had gathered in a tight knot in the most sheltered corner, and had been driven into the newly fashioned sheepfold. And at the end of the day Madeline and Bella had retired to bed with severe colds – but not before having their chests rubbed with goose grease and being dosed with elderberry rob.

Late at night the farmer had taken the hurricane lamp and trudged up the field to see that all was well. There was no snow on the ground yet but John could feel it was on the way and knew he had done the right thing. Seeing the steam rising from the wool backs, he had felt satisfied with all but one animal – a Welsh Black ewe who was showing signs of early lambing. She belonged to Spenser.

Now, still with eyes half-closed from clinging sleep, Spenser reluctantly levered himself into his working clothes. He swallowed the hot sweet tea his mother had poured out for him in the kitchen, pulled on his boots, coat and sou'wester, took the shepherd's staff from behind the door, lifted the latch and stepped out into a blinding white world.

For a full minute the boy stood motionless, astonished. He must be dreaming! The farm he had lived on all his life was no longer one he recognised. Some of its shape was familiar but most of its features lay hidden from sight, the yard and the buildings, the fields and the trees all painted over in cotton-wool white. There was no sound anywhere in that white world except for the scraping of shovels as the ground was found beneath the piled up snowdrifts; nor was there any movement in the farmyard except from his father, Edmund and Jack the odd-boy, all of them shovelling snow as though their lives depended on its immediate removal. There had been snow many a winter, but never anything like this. For the time being it had stopped, but the sky was flat and heavy and ready to drop some more.

A sense of urgency shook the boy into action. His ewe was in danger and if he didn't go at once it might be too late. He took a spade from the stable where the snow had just been cleared, forced open the orchard gate and stood looking at what appeared to be impassable white hillocks piled up against the trees. He looked along the hedge-side nearest the garden. There was less snow there, since the north-easter had blown it in the other direction; but it was a long way round to get to the sheep. If only he was as tall as Billy Six-Foot. Billy Six-Foot – where was he? One thing was certain, he was not in his accustomed place, the cow house; which meant that even with his height, William Saunders had not been able to negotiate the snowdrifts between his cottage and Seechem. It also meant there would be a lot more to do for all of them, thought Spenser, as he plunged on along the hedge-side.

Showers of snow fell on his shoulders as he brushed against the branches; without warning, his feet sank into drifts where drainage cut the banks; and lumps of snow dropped down his neck and into his boots. After what seemed like hours he reached the sheepfold only to find the entrance blocked by a thick wall of snow. He was about to drive his spade into it when it occurred to him that nature's wall was very efficiently keeping the wind out and the warmth in; so he turned and made his way round the fold to the top of the claypit, shovelling out steps as he went and clinging to branches for support.

He found the wider space between the trees, positioned himself and slid down the incline straight into the flock of steaming and very surprised sheep. For a second there was chaos; then, as the animals retreated into the corner furthest away from the intruder, a small tragedy was revealed in the little space they had left. There lay Two, not the original Welsh Black bought at Bromsgrove Fair five years before, but her daughter who had inherited the name when her mother died bringing her into the world. Since then Two had successfully borne lambs each year. But now beside the black still body lay two smaller ones, lambs which appeared as dead as the ewe.

Since a very small child no-one remembered seeing Spenser cry. He never intended that anyone should; and to protect himself from what he thought would be humiliation, he had built up a façade, a hardness of manner which deceived others into thinking he did not care. There was no-one watching now, only the silly sheep; and he let the tears fall, relieving the painful lump lodged in his throat. Full of sadness, Spenser gazed at the tiny black bodies.

Then suddenly he was stooping down, sweeping up first one lamb, then the other, into the warmth of his coat and body, keeping them close under the same arm. For one of them had momentarily twitched, he would swear, and instantly there flooded into his mind memories of other lambs taken for dead but miraculously brought to life by his mother.

With his free hand Spenser hauled himself out of the shelter to find that the sky had dropped a curtain of impenetrable swirling snowflakes so that now he could not even see the farm. He staggered uncertainly along the hedge-side with the two limp bodies under his arm. Making his way down the slope proved so formidable a task that when he reached the bottom he sat down in the snow and wondered despairingly whether he would ever see his home again. A numbing cold bemused his mind and had it not been for another unexpected twitch of life beneath his arm he might have given way to a desire to give up the battle and stay put.

How it was he reached the duck pond between Seechem and Rowney Green Farm, found his way around the perimeter and forced himself forward along the hedge leading to the orchard, he never really knew. His eyelids were like weights, two white mats spread across his brows and lashes, his muscles ached and his feet were frozen. By the time he reached the kitchen door he was incapable of lifting the latch, standing there immobile like some cardboard figure glued to a dirty white paper ground.

From within, Victoria thought she heard a sound. She had been listening for her second son with every nerve on edge, and this was not the first time she had run across the kitchen hoping to find him home again. She opened the door, at first no more than a crack, for the storm was making its way in at every conceivable point. Then she grabbed Spenser by the arm and pulled him into the warmth; she took off his outer garments covered completely in snow, and flung them into a corner. The lambs she laid in the hearth.

Pushing her son into a chair as near to the fire as possible, she ran for her brandy substitute, added hot water from the kettle on the hob and made him drink the peppery mixture. The blood began to flow warm in the boy's arteries, but instead of reviving he slumped in his seat and fell immediately into a sound sleep. Satisfied that it was sleep and not collapse, Victoria turned her attention to the lambs.

They seemed not to have moved. She lifted one little creature gently and held it directly over the smoke rising from the burning wood in the grate. It was only a moment before it coughed weakly, then spluttered and bleated. The smoke had irritated the nostrils and lungs and the lamb had pronounced itself alive just as a newborn baby cries out with life when it is held upside down and smacked. The farmer's wife rubbed the limbs and massaged the ribs until the little limp body began to stir. Then she wrapped it in a piece of old blanket and placed it back in the hearth. Without pausing she began carefully to repeat the operation with the second lamb.

When John and the other two came in, Victoria was frying thick slices of bacon for breakfast and Spenser was still asleep in the chair. The men looked down on the lambs.

'Gin's better than smoke to get 'em moving, me wench', was John's only remark.

from

The Cuckoo Clock

IRIS LESLIE

The industrious Benedictine nuns of Stanbrook Abbey near Worcester put their hands to many tasks, and they even run their own Stanbrook Abbey Press. One of its most

appealing productions was in 1987 – an anthology of verse entitled The Cuckoo Clock and other Poems *by the late Sir Shane Leslie, a first cousin of Sir Winston Churchill. The poems – including the two with a Christmas flavour reproduced here – were collected into book form by Sir Shane's widow, Lady Iris Leslie, who, as her Foreword explains, dedicated them as a Christmas present to her great-grandchildren, Heather Oriel, William, Cian and Olivia Maude.*

My dear Children

This is a collection of poems written by your great-grandfather whose name was Shane Leslie.

He was a grand person for you to think of as your forebear, tall and very splendid to look at, and always wearing his Irish kilt. He loved talking to children and telling them all sorts of exciting and interesting stories, and he often made them laugh and enjoy the funny side of things.

He would have delighted in you his great-grandchildren; I am sure he knows about you wherever he is and keeps a watchful eye on you all.

He wrote a large number of books which you will be able to read when you are older, and you will learn a great deal from them. He wrote a lot of poetry too, and I have chosen this collection to make a Christmas present for you. I hope very much you will enjoy the poems.

Your loving step-great-grandmother,

Iris Leslie

CHRISTMAS DANCE

Now Holly be King in the Song that we sing;
So Holly be King of the Christmas tide!
His Sceptre he flicks with a leafage of pricks
And a Crown of red berries he carries in pride.

Come rise up, you Masters – rise Men, to the dance.
Come gallants and all who feel gay – take your stance!
For Holly is King of the dancing ring
King of the gliding heel
King of the rollicking reel
Oh Holly is King – is King!

Sing Mistletoe Queen in her apple treen:
For Mistletoe's Queen of the Christmastide!
Her Sceptre's a stalk and as white as the chalk
Is the glimmering Orb that all Lovers have eyed.

Come Ladies, come Lasses, straight into our arms,
The Queen from the Castle, the girls from the farms!
For the Mistletoe's Queen in her robing of green
Queen of both Mistress and Miss
Queen of the Christmas Kiss —
Oh Mistletoe's Queen – the Queen!

CHRISTMAS IN HEAVEN

Where golden rain is gently pouring
And silver snow lies snug and soft:
The Christmas Tree with toys is soaring,
The Christchild giveth from aloft.

He gives unto the children poorest
The toys they dreamed but never had:
Unto the children of the dourest
To gypsies or forgotten mad.

And stars presenteth to the Wise Men
Who brought Him presents out of East:
But crusty Dons and panting Prize-men
He leaves outside the Christmas feast.

He hands out wooden swords to Fighters,
Who fought for what they once thought best:
To Curates silver-paper mitres
And ribbons for each Statesman's breast.

All Souls desirous get their wishes
In sorry sort of childish way:
But they will share God's life delicious
And Christmas with the Christchild play.

from

Country Calendar

GODFREY BASELEY

Godfrey Baseley was born in 1904 in what was then the small Worcestershire village of Alvechurch. An acknowledged authority on country life, he became a broadcaster on farming matters, and in 1950 created the BBC's radio serial The Archers. *Among his books is an*

· A Worcestershire Christmas ·

evocative commentary on the countryside entitled Country Calendar *in which he chronicles a year of rural life seen through the eyes of his gamekeeper friend, Tom Artwright. This extract reflects his thoughts on winter and Christmas.*

As the month moved on towards Christmas the winds shifted from the northerly direction, where they had stayed for most of the first week, to a more westerly direction, bringing milder weather, mists and some rain. The ponds that had been dry for so long were seen to be holding water once again, and here and there small pools lay in the ditches. There was no flow of water though to be seen flowing through the drainage pipes where they emptied themselves into the ditches.

'It'll take a heavy fall of snow and a slow thaw afore we shall see them flowing again,' was Tom's comment. 'It's a long time since I saw the ground so dry at this time of the year. It certainly looks as though we are leading up to a "green" Christmas, and you knows what they says about that, don't you? A green Christmas and a full churchyard.'

It was a green Christmas and for several days before, the whole of the countryside was enveloped in a thick mist. For a short time each day the pale winter sun was able to break through to cast long ghostlike shadows from the bare trees.

Although the invasion of the fieldfares had seemed to strip all the district bare of berries, bunches of mistletoe and branches of holly both bearing berries began to appear.

In the village, Christmas trees could be seen in the windows of the cottages, and from the coloured fairy lights that formed an important part of their decoration, shafts of multi-coloured light pierced the darkness to light up and be absorbed by the enveloping mist.

In the Bull the decorations had gone up to hide the tobacco-stained walls and ceilings. Extra supplies of drinks and fancy packs of cigarettes lined the shelves behind the bar, and on the

161

· *A Worcestershire Christmas* ·

night of the annual Christmas draw the whole place was crowded to capacity, each one hopeful of taking home some of the top prizes that had tempted them to subscribe.

During the days before Christmas, the 'dark' days, Tom had made his annual round to deliver presents of a brace of pheasants to the tenant farmers and all who had in any way contributed to the success of the shooting season. Amongst them was the roadman, now retired, who for so many years had kept a watchful eye open for anything untoward that might have happened to the game.

'The number of folks to call on gets less every year. At one time there were over forty tenants on the estate, now there's only twelve. Over the years as the old ones have died out, the farms have either been brought into hand or have been amalgamated with their neighbours. I can slip round them all in a couple of evenings in my Land Rover. When I first had the job to do, I used to go around in a horse and float, with the birds that the squire had helped to select and label, laid out on a bed of straw in the bottom of the float.

162

'You was always welcome, too welcome sometimes, and I must admit that there were a few occasions when I was glad that the old horse knew his way home.

'Christmas morning was quite a time at the Manor in the old days. Apart from preparing for the big house parties that they usually had, there was parcels of groceries to be packed up and delivered to every house where the people worked on the estate. Very practical parcels they were. Tea, sugar, cheese, butter and all that sort of thing. Most of these parcels were delivered personally by her ladyship who was driven round the village by the coachman with a footman to carry the parcels.

'You know, it is strange to think that that all happened within my memory. What a change I have seen in my lifetime so far. Goodness knows what is still to come.'

On Boxing Day the hounds met as usual in the market town of Leobury, with hundreds of people turning up to enjoy the pageantry of the occasion. The black and white beamed façade of the Royal Oak, the wide street that was once the market place, and the ancient town hall standing up on its time-worn stilts is the perfect setting for such an occasion, and no doubt provided a wonderful opportunity to try out newly acquired cameras to get shots of the hounds being stroked by the children, or of the red-coated riders on their well-groomed, spirited horses. Back at home, the Boxing Day shoot was still a feature for the tenant farmers.

'One of the most enjoyable days of the year,' was Tom's assessment of the Boxing Day shoot. 'You don't have to worry too much about what might or might not go wrong or right. We usually follows the same old pattern that we have been doing for years. Walking up through what kale is still about and through some of the smaller coverts and young plantations in the morning, then a good break for lunch, then after they have done themselves proud, I takes them to take their stand at Fardon's Coppice, in the hope that we can put a few screamers over their heads that if they hit, they can talk about for the rest of the year.

'There was a time when we used to lay on a bit of ferreting for some of the young chaps, but that is a thing of the past now. Apart from me I doubt if there is anybody else in the village as keeps ferrets these days. We lets the members of the Gun Club have a go at the pigeons, hares and any rabbits that they might see on another part of the estate from where the farmers are shooting, and some of the members likes to come along with us to do a bit of "beating" and "picking up".

'There's nothing like a bit of exercise on a Boxing Day to get over the eating and drinking that has gone on during the previous day.'

After Christmas, the mild weather continued, the mists became thinner, the sun did its best to cheer us up and almost the last sound that I heard on the last day of the year, was the song of a thrush perched high upon the top of our pear tree.

Acknowledgements

Introductory sections are by David Green, using published and unpublished reference material and personal interviews.

The four extracts from Fred Archer's reminiscences are reprinted by permission of the author and *Warwickshire & Worcestershire Life*. A.E. Housman's poems are reproduced with acknowledgement to the Housman Society. *The Blacksmith's Daughter* by Susan Oldacre was first published in 1985 by Alan Sutton Publishing Ltd. and is quoted by permission of the author. The extracts from the *Archers* trilogy by Jock Gallagher, published by BBC Books in 1988, are reprinted by courtesy of the author. The passages from *The Season of the Year* and *Come Rain, Come Shine* by John Moore are reprinted by permission of the Peters Fraser and Dunlop Group Ltd. The items by Sir Edward and Lady Elgar are reproduced by courtesy of the Elgar Birthplace Trust. 'A Robin at Christmas' by Dr Geoffrey Nelson first appeared in *Worcestershire The County Magazine* and appears with the author's permission. *Swings and Roundabouts* is published by Pelham Books, © 1987 by Graham Dilley and Graham Otway. *A Wyre Forest Diary* by Simon Fletcher was published by Kenneth Tomkinson Ltd. in 1981 and the extracts appear by permission of the author and Mrs Audrey Tomkinson. The poem 'Father Christmas' is reprinted by permission of the Governor of Long Lartin Prison. The letter from *My Dear Ann* by Ann O'Day Maples is reproduced by permission of Mrs June Wightman. Passages from *The Christmas Box* by Francis Brett Young are reprinted by permission of the University of Birmingham. *Lock Keeper's*

Daughter by Pat Warner was first published in 1986 by Shepperton Swan Ltd. The Clock House, Upper Halliford, Shepperton, Middlesex, and is quoted with their permission. *Cast a Long Shadow* by Mary Pearce was published in 1977 by Macdonald and Jane's, and the extracts are reprinted with the author's permission. *A Haircut and a Shave* by Philip Green was published in 1974 by Vantage Press Inc., New York, and is quoted with acknowledgement to the author. 'The Christmas Tree' by Meinrad Craighead first appeared in *The Sign of the Tree* published in 1979 by Imprint Books Ltd. (Mitchell Beazley Publishers) and is reprinted with their permission and with acknowledgement to the author. *Kidderminster Since 1800* was first published in 1975 by Kenneth Tomkinson Ltd. and the extract is reprinted by permission of Mrs Audrey Tomkinson and George Hall. 'Wassailing the Winter Orchards' is from the records of the Worcestershire Naturalists' Club. 'The Long Hard Winter' is from *Seechem Chronicles* by W. Eileen Davies, published by Halfshire Books of Bromsgrove in 1990, and is reprinted with the publisher's permission. The poems from *The Cuckoo Clock* appear by courtesy of Lady Iris Leslie. *Country Calendar* by Godfrey Baseley was first published in 1975 by Sidgwick & Jackson, and is quoted by permission of the author and publisher. The following items first appeared in *Warwickshire and Worcestershire Life* and are reprinted with acknowledgement to the authors: 'A Season for Spectres' by Raymond Lamont Brown; 'Roll on Christmas' by Gilbert Moore; 'This Baby Business at Bethlehem' by Mervyn Charles-Edwards; 'Turkeys, Grouse and the Song of the Quail' by Charles Lines; 'A Nightingale at Christmas' by John Leslie; 'Festive Fare' by Roland Titmus. Although considerable effort has been made to trace and contact original authors, this has not proved possible in every case. To those writers who have remained elusive, the compiler and publishers offer grateful acknowledgement for the extracts reproduced.

Picture Credits

Title page and pages 18, 43, 74, 120, 126, 139, 146, 162 – *Warwickshire & Worcestershire Life*. Page 2 – Colebrook & Co. Collection. Pages 4, 40, 86, 132 – Fred Archer. Page 12 – from a drawing in Bromsgrove Library. Pages 19, 34, 72, 77, 78, 89, 94, 107, 111, 150 – Bill Meadows. Pages 37, 135 – Elgar Birthplace Trust. Page 38 – R.J. Collins Collection, Hereford & Worcester County Record Office. Page 45 – Chris Brooke-Harris/Warwickshire Nature Conservation Trust. Page 59 – Worcestershire County Cricket Club. Page 68 – Margaret Layton. Page 91 – University of Birmingham. Page 129 – Imprint Books Ltd. (Mitchell Beazley Publishers) with acknowledgement to Meinrad Craighead.